DANIEL KAPLAN

D1091553

START R IN CALCULUS

PROJECT MOSAIC

Cover Photo: . [Photo credit: Maya Hanna.]

To Netta, Liat, and Tamar.

Preface: Calculus and Calculation

It's no coincidence that "calculus" and "calculate" are similar. When you perform a calculation, you take information in one form — say 3×19 — and translate it into another, more readily interpreted form — 57. Similarly, calculus translates information about parts and about change into information about wholes and accumulation.

In the 17th and 18th centuries, when calculus was invented by Newton and others, today's familiar computers were unimaginable. Sensibly, the calculations were presented in a means suitable to the technology of those centuries: paper and quill. The calculus computations of that era involved the manipulation of symbols according to mathematically derived rules, for instance $x^2 \rightarrow 2x$.

REGLE II.

Pour les quantités multipliées.

La différence du produit de plusieurs quantités multipliées les unes par les autres, est égale à la somme des produits de la différence de chacune de ces quantités par le produit des autres.

Ainsi la différence de $a x$ est $x o + a d x$, c'est à dire $a d x$. Celle de $\overline{a + x} \times \overline{b - y}$ est $b d x - y d x - a d y - x d y$.

Figure 1: One of the many rules for the manipulation of symbols presented in the first calculus textbook in 1699, by the Marquis de l'Hopital. ("Regle" is French for "rule.")

These rules are still useful in important ways, but there are now other technologies for performing the computations of calculus. In addition to symbolic calculus, there is numerical calculus, which relies on simple arithmetic. Numerical calculus, tedious and impractically slow for a human, is easy work for a computer. Perhaps surprisingly, numerical calculus is also easier for many people to understand and carry out. As such, it provides a means to teach the concepts of calculus.

Numerical calculus is also more general than symbolic calculus. There are many sorts of problems for which symbolic calculus fails to provide an answer even for the most talented and well-trained mathematicians. By using numerical calculus, a much wider range of problems can be addressed, even by beginners. This is especially true for modern problems in modeling and data analysis for which the symbolic methods were never intended.

Performing numerical calculus requires a computer. Less obviously, it also requires a way to communicate with the computer, to tell the computer what to do. In other words, to do calculus numerically, you need a way to translate between human intention and electronic computation: a language or notation.

These notes introduce one such notation for numerical calculus, based on the computer language R.

R IS A LANGUAGE for communicating instructions to a computer and, it turns out, is also effective for communicating with people. The R software is a computer system that understands this language and acts on it.

Many people get nervous when they hear they will be learning a new language. Most of our interaction with computers — word processing, e-mail, blogs and social networking, spreadsheets — is done with software that's menu- and mouse-driven. Typically, it's pretty easy to learn such systems. You just have to be shown how and it takes a few minutes to get started.

You will be spending a few **hours** getting started in R. Why? Isn't there some simpler way? Why isn't there nice mouse-based software? Why do you need to learn a language?

The answer isn't about the quality of software or the availability of friendly packages. Instead, the reason to learn a language has to do with the sorts of things you will be doing in mathematics and statistics. In themselves, the individual tasks you will undertake are not necessarily more complicated than, say, changing a word to a bold-face font, something you would do easily with a mouse.

THERE ARE SEVERAL ASPECTS OF TECHNICAL COMPUT-
ING that makes it different from word-processing and
other familiar, everyday computing tasks.

1. In mathematics and statistics, there are often multiple
   inputs to a computation. To illustrate multiple inputs,
   consider a familiar word-processing computation: finding all the instances of the word "car" in a document
   and changing them to "automobile". Easy enough; just
   use the FIND feature. But be careful! You might end
   up with "automobileeful" or "inautomobilecerated" or
   "automobilecinogenic" instead of careful, incarcerated,
   or carcinogenic. A second input to the calculation is
   needed: the set of contexts in which to allow or disal-
   low the change. For instance, allow the change when
   "car" is preceded by a space and followed by a space
   or a period or a comma, or an "s" + space ("cars" →
   "automobiles"). Things are not so simple as they might
   seem at first, which is why the find-and-replace feature
   of word-processors is only partially effective.

2. In mathematics and statistics, the output of one computation often becomes the input to another computation. That's why math courses spend so much time
   talking about functions (and "domain" and "range",
   etc.). In word processing, whenever you highlight a
   word and move it or change the font or replace it, you
   still end up with stuff on which you can perform the
   same operations: highlighting, moving, font-changing,
   etc. Not so in math and statistics. The sorts of operations that you will often perform — solving, integration, statistical summaries, etc. — produce a new kind
   of thing on which you will be performing new kinds
   of operations. In mathematics and statistics, you create a chain of operations and you need to be able to
   express the steps in that chain. It's not a question of
   having enough buttons to list all the operations, you'll
   need combinations of operations — more than could
   possibly be listed in a menu system.

3. In mathematics and statistics, the end-product is not
   the only thing of importance. When you write a letter or post to a blog, what counts is the final product,
   not the changes you made while writing and certainly

not the thought process that you went through in composing your words. But in mathematics and statistics, the end-product is the result of a chain of calculations and it's important that each step in that chain be correct. Therefore, it's important that each step in the chain be documented and reproducible so that it can be checked, updated, and verified. Often, the chain of calculations becomes a new computation that you might want to apply to a new set of inputs. Expressing your calculations as a language allows you to do this.

If you have ever travelled to a country where you don't speak the language, you know that you can communicate simple ideas with gestures and pointing and can satisfy the relatively simply expressed needs of eating and hygiene and shelter. But when you want to converse with a person and express rich ideas, you need a shared language.

Many people think that it would be better if other people learned our language, and the natural extension of this is that computers should be taught to speak English. But it turns out that English, or other natural languages, are not set up to be effective at communicating mathematical or statistical ideas. You need to learn a way to do this. The algebraic notation taught in high school is part of the story, but not a complete solution. That's why you'll be learning R.

If you've ever learned just a little of a foreign language, you're familiar with the situation where you say something that seems straightforward, but your listener gives you a quizzical look: it doesn't make sense. You used the wrong verb or the wrong preposition or a word with a slightly different meaning. A relative of mine, visiting me in France, once asked my host about "last year," or so he intended. He actually said something pretty close to "elder buttock." This did not produce the intended reaction.

Similarly in R. At first, you will make elementary mistakes. The computer will respond, like my French host, quizzically. But with practice — just a few hours — you will become fluent and able to express your ideas with confidence and certainty.

As you learn the R language, which will be much, much easier than learning a natural language like French or Chinese or Spanish, you will make mistakes and you will run into frustrating situations. But remember, the reason you are learning it is to be able to express complicated ideas. It's the nature of mathematics and statistics that's at the core here. Having a systematic way to express yourself will not only let you use the computer's power, but will increase your understanding of the mathematical and statistical ideas.

My thanks go to my colleagues at Macalester, particularly Dan Flath and Chad Topaz, and the scores of students from Math 135 who tested this material and provided many suggestions for improvements. Randall Pruim and Nicholas Horton have been instrumental in transforming sketchy software ideas into the mosaic package. This work was supported in part by Project MOSAIC and, especially, a grant from the US National Science Foundation (DUE-0920350).
— Daniel Kaplan, Dec. 2012

Contents

1. Starting with RStudio

R is a language that you can use to direct a computer to perform mathematical and statistical operations, produce graphics, carry out data processing. In between the language and the computer is a system that interprets the language and communicates your instructions to the computer's operating system and hardware. Due to the popularity of R, there are many such interpreters. The one you will be using is called **RStudio**.

You will likely use **RStudio** as a web service, like Facebook or Google Docs.[1] You need only have an Internet connection and a recent web browser — the sort of thing you might use for Facebook. No other software installation is required.

[1] It's also possible to install RStudio on your own computer, and to use it without the web.

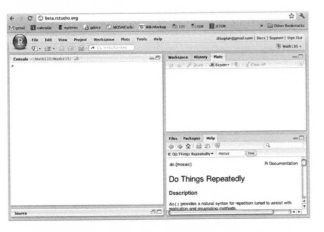

Figure 2: The RStudio window displayed in a web browser.

The RStudio window has the familiar menu bar and is divided into four "panes":

1. The **Console** pane, into which you will type your

commands. The console maintains a transcript of your session with RStudio — your command inputs and the computer's response.

2. The **Workspace/History/Plots** pane, which contains three tabs. The **Plots** tab is where your graphics will appear. **History** maintains an organized record of your previous commands to help you remember.

3. The **Files/Packages/Help** pane, which allows you to access documentation of commands as well as to load in new specialized software ("packages").

4. The **Source** pane, barely visible in the figure, which you will not be using at first. Among other things, "source" provides an editor for writing computer programs, which are chains of commands stored for later re-use.

Ready? Go to the console and give your first command, right after the prompt >.

```
3+2
```

When you press return, R interprets your command and gives its response.

```
[1] 5
```

Simple arithmetic in R is done with a familiar notation. (See Figure 3 for some examples.) Remember to use $*$ multiplication and $\hat{\ }$ for exponentiation. Multiplication must always be specified explicitly. It's correct to say 6*(3+1) but invalid to say 6(3+1).

```
5-2                    3^2                    9*6+1
[1] 3                  [1] 9                  [1] 55
5/2                    9*7                    9*(6+1)
[1] 2.5                [1] 63                 [1] 63
2^3
[1] 8
```

Figure 3: Arithmetic in R

For functions with letter names, for instance cos and ln, you put the input to the function between parentheses. For instance:

```
sqrt(9)                acos(0)                log(10)
[1] 3                  [1] 1.571              [1] 2.303
cos(1)                 sin(pi)                exp(-3)
[1] 0.5403             [1] 1.225e-16          [1] 0.04979
```

Figure 4: Use parentheses to provide the input to named functions.

OFTEN, YOU WILL WANT TO STORE the result of a calculation under a name so that you can re-use the result later. Such storage is called "assignment" and is accomplished with the = operator:

```
first = 3
second = 4
hypot = sqrt(first^2 + second^2)
myangle = asin(second/hypot)
hypot*cos(myangle)

[1] 3
```

When you want to see the value of a named value, just type the name as a command:

```
hypot
```

```
[1] 5
```

Of course, R can do much more than such calculations, but that's enough to start for now.

IMPORTANT NOTE ABOUT TYPING: In the RStudio console, you can use the keyboard up- and down-arrows to recall previous statements. That saves you some typing when you want to repeat something, or to make a small change to a previous command. Remember that the console is in the form of a dialog, not a document. Each new command, even if it is an edited version of a previous command, appears on the last line. The up- and down-arrows copy previous commands to the current prompt line, but you can't edit the past, just copy it.

Exercises

EXERCISE 1 Use R to calculate a numerical value for each of these arithmetic expressions:

(a) `3*sqrt(97)`
13.72   21.61   23.14   29.55   31.01   31.20   33.03

(b) `sqrt(pi)`
1.6152   1.7693   1.7725   1.8122   3.1416   3.519

(c) `exp(pi)`
13.72   21.61   23.14   29.55   31.01   31.20   33.03

(d) `pi^3`
13.72   21.61   23.14   29.55   31.01   31.20   33.03

EXERCISE 2 Use R to calculate a numerical value for each of these arithmetic expressions:

(a) $\sqrt{2/3}$
0.4805   0.5173   0.5642   0.6304   0.7071   0.8165

(b) $\cos \pi/4$
0.4805   0.5173   0.5642   0.6304   0.7071   0.8165

(c) $1/\sqrt{2}$
0.4805   0.5173   0.5642   0.6304   0.7071   0.8165

(d) $1/\sqrt{\pi}$
0.4805   0.5173   0.5642   0.6304   0.7071   0.8165

(e) $10^{-1/\pi}$
0.4805   0.5173   0.5642   0.6304   0.7071   0.8165

EXERCISE 3 Here is a set of R expressions that you should cut and paste as a command into your R session:

```
alpha = 7
beta = 3
x = 9
```

From these named quantities, you are going to compute a new one:

```
res=atan(sqrt(alpha^2-beta)+
    tan(x/alpha+beta/x))
```

You don't have to worry about what the last expression might possibly mean, it's just intended to be something complicated. Make sure to cut and paste it into R so that you get it exactly right.

The value of `res` will be −1.4991. Before continuing, make sure that your value matches this, otherwise you won't get correct answers for the following questions.

(a) Change `alpha` to 17 and recompute `res`. What's the new value of `res`? (Hint: Use the up arrow to recall the complicated command.)
1.5099   1.5127   1.5155   1.5177   1.5182   1.5207

(b) Keep `alpha` at 17 and x at 9, but change `beta` to 6.6. Recompute `res`. What's the new value of `res`?
1.5099   1.5127   1.5155   1.5177   1.5182   1.5207

(c) Keep `alpha` at 17 and `beta` at 6.6, but change x to 1. Recompute `res`. What's the new value of `res`?
1.5099   1.5127   1.5155   1.5177   1.5182   1.5207

(d) Keep `alpha` at 17 and `beta` at 6.6, but change x to −1. Recompute `res`. What's the new value of `res`?
1.5099   1.5127   1.5155   1.5177   1.5182   1.5207

2. Functions & Graphing

2.1 Graphing Mathematical Functions

In this lesson, you will learn how to use R to **graph mathematical functions**.

It's important to point out at the beginning that much of what you will be learning — much of what will be new to you here — actually has to do with the mathematical structure of functions and not R.

Recall that a function is a transformation from an input to an output. Functions are used to represent the relationship between quantities. In **evaluating a function**, you specify what the input will be and the function translates it into the output.

In much of the traditional mathematics notation you have used, functions have names like f or g or y, and the input is notated as x. Other letters are used to represent **parameters**. For instance, it's common to write the equation of a line this way

$$y = mx + b.$$

In order to apply mathematical concepts to realistic settings in the world, it's important to recognize three things that a notation like $y = mx + b$ does not support well:

1. Real-world relationships generally involve more than two quantities. (For example, the Ideal Gas Law in chemistry, $PV = nRT$, involves three variables: pressure, volume, and temperature.) For this reason, you will need a notation that lets you describe the *multiple inputs* to a function and which lets you keep track of which input is which.

The MOSAIC package.

You will be using a handful of functions in R, such as `plotFun()` and `makeFun()`, many of which are provided by the `mosaic` add-on package. To use these functions, you must first tell R to load the package. This can be done with this R command.

```
require(mosaic)
```

If you get an error message, it is likely because the package has not yet been installed on your computer. Doing so is easy:

```
install.packages("mosaic")
```

You need install the package only once. (It may already have been done for you.) But you need to load the `mosaic` package each time you restart R.

2. Real-world quantities are not typically named x and y, but are quantities like "cyclic AMP concentration" or "membrane voltage" or "government expenditures". Of course, you could call all such things x or y, but it's much easier to make sense of things when the names remind you of the quantity being represented.

3. Real-world situations involve many different relationships, and mathematical models of them can involve different approximations and representations of those relationships. Therefore, it's important to be able to give names to relationships, so that you can keep track of the various things you are working with.

For these reasons, the notation that you will use needs to be more general than the notation commonly used in high-school algebra. At first, this will seem odd, but the oddness doesn't have to do so much with the fact that the notation is used by the computer so much as for the mathematical reasons given above.

But there is one aspect of the notation that stems directly from the use of the keyboard to communicate with the computer. In writing mathematical operations, you'll use expressions like a*b and 2^n and a/b rather than the traditional ab or 2^n or $\frac{a}{b}$, and you will use parentheses both for grouping expressions and for applying functions to their inputs.

In plotting a function, you need to specify several things:

What is the function. This is usually given by an expression, for instance m*x + b or A*x^2 or sin(2*t) Later on, you will also give names to functions and use those names in the expressions, much like sin is the name of a trigonometric function.

What are the inputs. Remember, there's no reason to assume that x is always the input, and you'll be using variables with names like G and cAMP. So you have to be explicit in saying what's an input and what's not. The R notation for this involves the ~ ("tilde") symbol. For instance, to specify a linear function with x as the input, you can write m*x + b ~ x

What range of inputs to make the plot over. Think of this as the bounds of the horizontal axis over which you want to make the plot.

The values of any parameters. Remember, the notation m*x+b ~ x involves not just the variable input x but also two other quantities, m and b. To make a plot of the function, you need to pick specific values for m and b and tell the computer what these are.

The plotFun() operator puts this all together, taking the information you give and turning it into a plot. Here's an example of plotting out a linear function:

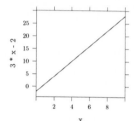

```
plotFun(3*x - 2 ~ x, x.lim=range(0,10) )
```

Often, it's natural to write such relationships with the parameters represented by symbols. (This can help you remember which parameter is which, e.g., which is the slope and which is the intercept. When you do this, remember to give a specific numerical value for the parameters, like this:

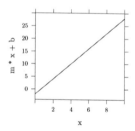

```
plotFun(m*x + b ~ x, x.lim=range(0,10), m=3, b=-2 )
```

Try these examples:

```
plotFun(A*x^2 ~ x, x.lim=range(-2,3), A=10)
plotFun(A*x^2 ~ x, add=TRUE, col="red", A=5)
plotFun(cos(t) ~ t, t.lim=range(0,4*pi))
```

Sometimes, you want to give a function a name so that you can refer to it concisely later on. You can use makeFun() to create a function and ordinary assignment to give the function a name. For instance:

```
g = makeFun(2*x^2 - 5*x + 2 ~ x)
```

Once the function is named, you can evaluate it by giving an input. For instance:

```
g(x=2)
```
```
[1] 0
```

```
g(x=5)
```
```
[1] 27
```

To plot g(), you need to provide an argument and use the ~ to identify which variable corresponds to the x-axis.

```
plotFun(g(x) ~ x, x.lim=range(-5,5))
```

Exercises

EXERCISE 1 This command

```
plotFun(A*x^2 ~ A, A.lim=range(-2,3), x=10)
```

will graph a straight line. Explain why the graph doesn't look like a parabola, even though it's a graph of Ax^2.

EXERCISE 2
Translate each of these expressions in traditional math notation into a plot made by plotFun(). Hand in the command that you gave to make the plot (not the plot itself).

(a) $4x - 7$ in the window x from 0 to 10.

(b) $\cos 5x$ in the window x from -1 to 1.

(c) $\cos 2t$ in the window t from 0 to 5.

(d) $\sqrt{t}\cos 5t$ in the window t from 0 to 5. (Hint: $\sqrt{(t)}$ is sqrt(t).)

EXERCISE 3 Find the value of each of the functions in EXERCISE 2 at $x = 10.543$ or at $t = 10.543$. (Hint: Give the function a name and compute the value using an expression like g(x=10.543) or f(t=10.543).)
Pick the closest numerical value

(a) 32.721 34.721 35.172 37.421 37.721

(b) -0.83 -0.77 -0.72 -0.68 0.32 0.42 0.62

(c) -0.83 -0.77 -0.72 -0.68 -0.62 0.42 0.62

(d) -2.5 -1.5 -0.5 0.5 1.5 2.5

EXERCISE 4
Reproduce each of these two plots. Hand in the command you used to make the identical plots:

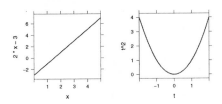

EXERCISE 5
What happens when you use a symbolic parameter (e.g., m in m*x + b ~ x, but try to make a plot without selecting a specific numerical value for the parameter?

EXERCISE 6
What happens when you don't specify a range for an input, but just a single number, as in the second of these two commands:

```
plotFun(3*x ~ x, x.lim=range(1,4))
plotFun(3*x ~ x, x.lim=14)
```

Give a description of what happened and speculate on why.

2.2 *Making Scatterplots from Data*

Often, the mathematical models that you will create will be motivated by data. For a deep appreciation of the relationship between data and models, you will want to study statistical modeling. Here, though, we will take a first cut at the subject in the form of **curve fitting**, the process of setting parameters of a mathematical function to make the function a close representation of some data.

This means that you will have to learn something about how to access data in computer files, how data are stored, and how to visualize the data. Fortunately, R and the mosaic package make this straightforward.

The data files you will be using are stored as **spreadsheets** on the Internet. Typically, the spreadsheet will have multiple variables; each variable is stored as one column. (The rows are "cases," sometimes called "data points.") To read the data in to R, you need to know the name of the file and its location.

The function for reading such files from their appointed place on the Internet is called fetchData().

One of the files that fetchData() can read is "Income-Housing.csv". This file gives information from a survey on housing conditions for people in different income brackets in the US.[2] Here's how to read it into R:

```
housing = fetchData("Income-Housing.csv")
```

There are two important things to notice about the above statement. First, the fetchData() function is returning a value that is being stored in an object called housing. The choice of housing as a name is arbitrary; you could have stored it as x or Equador or whatever. It's convenient to pick names that help you remember what's being stored where.

Second, the name "Income-Housing.csv" is surrounded by quotation marks. These are the single-character double quotes, that is, " and not repeated single quotes ' '. Whenever you are reading data from a file, the name of the file should be in such single-character double quotes. That way, R knows to treat the characters literally and not as the name of an object such as housing.

[2] Susan E. Mayer (1997) *What money can't buy: Family income and children's life chances* Harvard Univ. Press p. 102.

ONCE THE DATA are read in, you can look at the data just by typing the name of the object (without quotes!) that is holding the data. For instance,

```
housing
```

	Income	IncomePercentile	CrimeProblem	AbandonedBuildings
1	3914	5	39.6	12.6
2	10817	15	32.4	10.0
3	21097	30	26.7	7.1
4	34548	50	23.9	4.1
5	51941	70	21.4	2.3
6	72079	90	19.9	1.2

All of the variables in the dataset will be shown (although just four of them are printed here).

You can see the names of *all of the variables* in a compact format with the names() command:

```
names(housing)
```

```
 [1] "Income"              "IncomePercentile"    "CrimeProblem"
 [4] "AbandonedBuildings"  "IncompleteBathroom"  "NoCentralHeat"
 [7] "ExposedWires"        "AirConditioning"     "TwoBathrooms"
[10] "MotorVehicle"        "TwoVehicles"         "ClothesWasher"
[13] "ClothesDryer"        "Dishwasher"          "Telephone"
[16] "DoctorVisitsUnder7"  "DoctorVisits7To18"   "NoDoctorVisitUnder7"
[19] "NoDoctorVisit7To18"
```

When you want to access one of the variables, you give the name of the whole dataset followed by the name of the variable, with the two names separated by a $ sign, like this:

```
housing$Income
```

```
[1]   3914 10817 21097 34548 51941 72079
```

```
housing$CrimeProblem
```

```
[1] 39.6 32.4 26.7 23.9 21.4 19.9
```

Even though the output from names() shows the variable names in quotation marks, you won't use quotations around the variable names.

Spelling and capitalization are important. If you make a mistake, no matter how trifling to a human reader, R will not figure out what you want. For instance, here's a misspelling of a variable name, which results in nothing (that is, `NULL`) being returned.

```
housing$crim
```

```
NULL
```

Sometimes people like to look at datasets in a spreadsheet format, each entry in a little cell. In RStudio, you can do this by going to the WORKSPACE tab and clicking the name of the variable you want to look at.

	Income	IncomePercentile	CrimeProblem	AbandonedBuildings	IncompleteBathroom	NoCentralHeat
1	3914	5	39.6	12.6	2.6	32.3
2	10817	15	32.4	10.0	3.3	34.7
3	21097	30	26.7	7.1	2.3	28.1
4	34548	50	23.9	4.1	2.1	21.4
5	51941	70	21.4	2.3	2.4	14.9
6	72079	90	19.9	1.2	2.0	9.6

6 observations of 19 variables

Figure 5: Viewing a dataset by clicking on the object name in the WORKSPACE tab in RStudio.

It's hard to see patterns in columns of numbers, but a graphical presentation of data can be informative. One of the most familiar graphical forms is the **scatterplot**, a format in which each "case" or "data point" is plotted as a dot at the coordinate location given by two variables. For instance, here's a scatter plot of the percentage of household that regard their neighborhood as having a crime problem, versus the median income in their bracket.

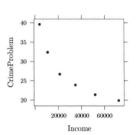

Figure 6: A scatterplot.

```
plotPoints( CrimeProblem ~ Income, data=housing )
```

The R statement closely follows the English equivalent: "plot `CrimeProblem` versus (or, as a function of) `Income`, using the data from the `housing` object.

If you want to plot a mathematical function **over** the data, do so by first giving a `plot` command to show the data, then asking `plotFun()` to add a graph of the function:

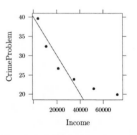

Figure 7: Adding a mathematical function to the scatterplot.

```
plotPoints( CrimeProblem ~ Income, data=housing )
plotFun( 40 - Income/2000 ~ Income,
        Income.lim=range(0,80000), add=TRUE )
```

The function drawn is not a very good match to the data, but this reading is about how to draw graphs, not how to choose a family of functions or find parameters! Notice the add=TRUE argument to plotFun(), which instructs R to add the new graph over the old one. Without this, R would draw a brand-new graph.

The plotFun() graph-drawing function allows you to give your mathematical function arguments of whatever name you like. So you could add another graph to the plot by giving a function like this:

```
plotFun( 38 - x/3500 ~ x, x.lim=range(0,80000), add=TRUE, col="red")
```

If, when plotting your data, you prefer to set the limits of the axes to something of your own choice, you can do this. For instance:

```
plotPoints( CrimeProblem ~ Income, data=housing,
            xlim=range(0,100000), ylim=range(0,50) )
plotFun( 40 - Income/2000 ~ Income,
         Income=range(0,80000), add=TRUE )
```

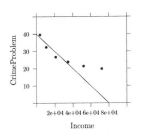

Properly made scientific graphics should have informative axis names. You can set the axis names directly in either plotFun() or plotPoints():

```
plotPoints( CrimeProblem ~ Income/1000, data=housing,
    xlab="Income Bracket (USD/year)",
    ylab="Percentage of Households",
    main="Crime Problem",
    xlim=range(0,100), ylim=range(0,45) )
```

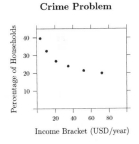

Notice that double-quotes delimit the character strings. The argument names xlim, ylim, xlab and ylab are used to refer to the ranges and labels of the horizontal and vertical axes respectively.

Exercises

EXERCISE 1

Make each of these plots:

(a) Prof. Stan Wagon (see
http://stanwagon.com) illustrates curve
fitting using measurements of the
temperature (in degrees C) of a cup of
coffee versus time (in minutes):

```
s = fetchData("stan-data.csv")
plotPoints(temp ~ time, data=s)
```

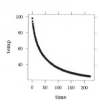

Describe in everyday English the pattern
you see in coffee cooling:

(b) Here's a record of the tide level in Hawaii
over about 100 hours:

```
h = fetchData("hawaii.csv")
plotPoints(water ~ time, data=h)
```

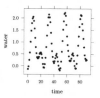

Describe in everyday English the pattern
you see in the tide data:

EXERCISE 2

Construct the R commands to duplicate
each of these plots. Hand in your commands
(not the plot):

(a) The data file "utilities.csv" has utility
records for a house in St. Paul, Minnesota,
USA. Make this plot, including the labels:

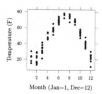

(b) From the "utilities.csv" data file, make
this plot of household monthly bill for
natural gas versus average temperature.
The line has slope -5 \$US/degree and
intercept 300 \$US.

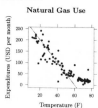

2.3 Graphing Functions of Two Variables

You've already seen how to plot a graph of a function of
one variable, for instance:

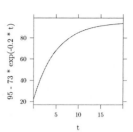

```
plotFun(95-73*exp(-.2*t) ~ t,
        t.lim=range(0,20))
```

This lesson is about plotting functions of two
variables. For the most part, the format used will be a
contour plot, but it's also possible to make the graph of
the function, as you'll see later.

You use the same plotFun() function to plot with two
input variables. The only change is that you need to list
the two variables on the right of the ~ sign, and you need
to give a range for each of the variables. For example:

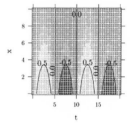

```
plotFun( sin(2*pi*t/10)*exp(-.2*x) ~ t & x,
         t.lim=range(0,20),x.lim=range(0,10))
```

Each of the contours is labeled, and by default the plot
is filled with color to help guide the eye. If you prefer just
to see the contours, without the color fill, use the
filled=FALSE argument.

```
plotFun( sin(2*pi*t/10)*exp(-.2*x) ~ t & x,
         t.lim=range(0,20),x.lim=range(0,10),filled=FALSE)
```

Occasionally, people want to see the function as a
surface, plotted in 3 dimensions. You can get the
computer to display a perspective 3-dimensional plot by
giving the optional argument surface=TRUE.

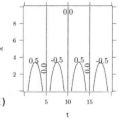

```
plotFun(sin(2*pi*t/10)*exp(-.2*x) ~ t & x,
        t.lim=range(0,20),x.lim=range(0,10),surface=TRUE)
```

If you are using RStudio, you can press on the little
gear icon ✳ in the plot and you will have a slider to
control the viewpoint. (Try moving the slider to the right,
release it, and wait for the picture to update.)

It's very hard to read quantitative values from a
surface plot — the contour plots are much more useful
for that. On the other hand, people seem to have a strong

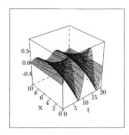

intuition about shapes of surfaces. Being able to translate in your mind from contours to surfaces (and *vice versa*) is a valuable skill.

SOMETIMES YOU WILL WANT TO CREATE AND PLOT a named function. When the function has multiple arguments, you need to be aware of which argument is which when you plot it, or you might get them reversed. Here's a safe strategy.

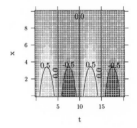

```
g = makeFun( sin(2*pi*t/10)*exp(-.2*x) ~ t & x)
plotFun(g(t=t,x=x) ~ t & x,
        t.lim=range(0,20),x.lim=range(0,10))
```

The point of the seemingly redundant t=t and x=x is to avoid mistaking the arguments one for the other. The name to the left of the = sign gives the name of the input variable. The expression g(t=t,x=x) says to assign the plotting variable t (which will range from 0 to 20) to the input named t.

So long as you use the input names, the order doesn't matter:

```
g(t=7,x=4)              g(x=4,t=7)

[1] -0.4273             [1] -0.4273
```

But if you don't use the names, you might end up assigning the input value to the wrong input:

```
g(7,4)                  g(4,7)

[1] -0.4273             [1] 0.1449
```

Exercises

EXERCISE 1

Refer to this contour plot:

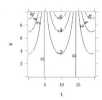

Approximately what is the value of the function at each of these (x, t) pairs? Pick the closest value

(a) $x = 4, t = 10$: -6 -5 -4 -2 0 2 4 5 6

(b) $x = 8, t = 10$: -6 -5 -4 -2 0 2 4 5 6

(c) $x = 7, t = 0$: -6 -5 -4 -2 0 2 4 5 6

(d) $x = 9, t = 0$: -6 -5 -4 -2 0 2 4 5 6

EXERCISE 2

Describe the shape of the contours produced by each of these functions. (Hint: Make the plot! Caution: Use the mouse to make the plotting frame more-or-less square in shape.)

(a) The function

```
plotFun( sqrt((v-3)^2+2*(w-4)^2) ~ v & w,
    v.lim=range(0,6),w.lim=range(0,6))
```

has contours that are
A   Parallel Lines
B   Concentric Circles
C   Concentric Ellipses
D   X Shaped

(b) The function

```
plotFun( sqrt( (v-3)^2+(w-4)^2 ) ~ v & w,
    v.lim=range(0,6),w.lim=range(0,6))
```

has contours that are
A   Parallel Lines
B   Concentric Circles
C   Concentric Ellipses
D   X Shaped

(c) The function

```
plotFun( 6*v-3*w+4 ~ v & w,
    v.lim=range(0,6),w.lim=range(0,6))
```

has contours that are:
A   Parallel Lines
B   Concentric Circles
C   Concentric Ellipses
D   X Shaped

2.4 *Splines & Smoothers*

Mathematical models attempt to capture patterns in the real world. This is useful because the models can be more easily studied and manipulated than the world itself. One of the most important uses of functions is to reproduce or capture or model the patterns that appear in data.

Sometimes, the choice of a particular form of function — exponential or power-law, say — is motivated by an understanding of the processes involved in the pattern that the function is being used to model. But other times, all that's called for is a function that follows the data and that has other desirable properties, for example is smooth or increases steadily.

"Smoothers" and "splines" are two kinds of general-purpose functions that can capture patterns in data, but for which there is no simple algebraic form. Creating such functions is remarkably easy, so long as you can free yourself from the idea that functions must always have algebraic formulas like $f(x) = ax^2 + b$.

Smoothers and splines are defined not by algebraic forms and parameters, but by data and algorithms. To illustrate, consider some simple data. The data set Loblolly contains 84 measurements of the age and height of loblolly pines.

```
pine = fetchData("Loblolly")
plotPoints(height ~ age,data=pine)
```

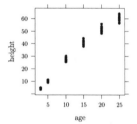

Several three-year old pines of very similar height were measured and tracked over time: age five, age ten, and so on. The trees differ from one another, but they are all pretty similar and show a simple pattern: linear growth at first which seems to slow down over time.

It might be interesting to speculate about what sort of algebraic function the loblolly pines growth follows, but any such function is just a model. For many purposes, measuring how the growth rate changes as the trees age, all that's needed is a smooth function that looks like the data. Let's consider two:

- A "cubic spline", which follows the groups of data points and curves smoothly and gracefully.

```
f1 = spliner(height ~ age, data=pine)
```

- A "linear interpolant", which connects the groups of data points with straight lines.

```
f2 = connector(height ~ age, data=pine)
```

The definitions of these functions may seem strange at first — they are entirely defined by the data: no parameters! Nonetheless, they are genuine functions and can be worked with like other functions. For example, you can put in an input and get an output:

```
f1(age=8)

[1] 20.68

f2(age=8)

[1] 20.55
```

You can graph them:

```
plotFun(f1(age) ~ age, age.lim=range(0,30))
plotFun(f2(age) ~ age, add=TRUE, col="red")
plotPoints(height ~ age, data=pine, add=TRUE)
```

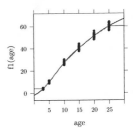

In all respects, these are perfectly ordinary functions. All respects but one: There is no simple formula for them. You'll notice this if you ever try to look at the computer-language definition of the functions:

```
f2

function (age)
{
    x <- get(fnames[2])
    if (connect)
        SF(x)
    else SF(x, deriv = deriv)
}
<environment: 0x1046c06d8>
```

There's almost nothing here to tell you what the function is. The definition refers to the data itself which has been stored in an "environment." These are computer-age functions, not functions from the age of algebra.

As you can see, the spline and linear connector functions are quite similar, except for the range of inputs outside of the range of the data. Within the range of the data, however, both types of functions go exactly through the center of each age-group.

Splines and connectors are not always what you will want, especially when the data are not divided into discrete groups, as with the loblolly pine data. For instance, the `trees` data set is measurements of the volume, girth, and height of black cherry trees. The trees were felled for their wood, and the interest in making the measurements was to help estimate how much usable volume of wood can be gotten from a tree, based on the girth (that is, circumference) and height. This would be useful, for instance, in estimating how much money a tree is worth. However, unlike the loblolly pine data, the black cherry data does not involve trees falling nicely into defined groups.

```
cherry = fetchData("trees")
plotPoints(Volume~Girth, data=cherry)
```

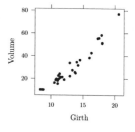

It's easy enough to make a spline or a linear connector:

```
g1 = spliner(Volume~Girth, data=cherry)
g2 = connector(Volume~Girth, data=cherry)
plotFun(g1(x)~x,x.lim=range(8,18),xlab="Girth (inches)")
plotFun(g2(x) ~ x, add=TRUE, col="red")
plotPoints(Volume ~ Girth, data=cherry, add=TRUE)
```

The two functions both follow the data ... but a bit too faithfully! Each of the functions insists on going through every data point. (The one exception is the two points with girth of 13 inches. There's no function that can go through both of the points with girth 13, so the functions split the difference and go through the average of the two points.)

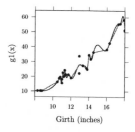

It's hard to believe that the rapid up-and-down wiggling is of the functions is realistic. When you have reason to believe that a smooth function is more appropriate than one with lots of ups-and-downs, a different type of function is appropriate: a smoother.

```
g3 = smoother(Volume ~ Girth, data=cherry, span=0.5)
plotFun(g3(x)~x,x.lim=range(8,18),xlab="Girth (inches)")
plotPoints(Volume~Girth, data=cherry, add=TRUE)
```

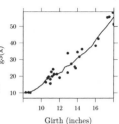

Smoothers are well named: they construct a smooth function that goes close to the data. You have some control over how smooth the function should be. The parameter span governs this:

```
g4 = smoother(Volume ~ Girth, data=cherry, span=1.0)
```

Of course, often you will want to capture relationships where there is more than one variable as the input. Smoothers do this very nicely; just specify which variables are to be the inputs.

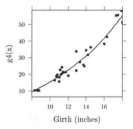

Figure 8: Control the smoothness of the curve with the span parameter.

```
g5 = smoother(Volume ~ Girth+Height, data=cherry,
              span=1.0)
plotFun(g5(g,h) ~ g & h,
        g.lim=range(8,18), h.lim=range(60,90))
```

When you make a smoother or a spline or a linear connector, remember these rules:

• You need a dataset containing the data.

• You use the formula with the variable you want as the output of the function on the left side of the tilde, and the input variables on the right side.

• The function that is created will have input names that match the variables you specified as inputs. (For the present, only smoother will accept more than one input variable.)

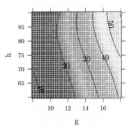

Figure 9: A smoother in two variables: Girth and Height.

• The smoothness of a smoother function can be set by the span argument. A span of 1.0 is typically pretty smooth. The default is 0.5.

- When creating a spline, you have the option of declaring monotonic=TRUE. This will arrange things to avoid extraneous bumps in data that shows a steady upward pattern or a steady downward pattern.

When you want to plot out a function, you need of course to choose a range for the input values. It's often sensible to select a range that corresponds to the data on which the function is based. You can find this with the max() and min() commands, e.g.

```
min(Height, data=cherry)      max(Height, data=cherry)

[1] 63                        [1] 87
```

Exercises

EXERCISE 1

The Orange data set contains data on the circumference and age of trees.

```
orange = fetchData("Orange")
names(orange)
[1] "Tree"          "age"
[3] "circumference"
```

(a) Construct a smoother of circumference (in cm) as a function of age (in days), with span=1. What's the value of the function for age 1000 days?

127.41 128.32 130.28 132.08 133.12 138.20

(b) Construct a smoother of circumference versus age with span=10. What's the value for age 1000 days?

127.41 128.32 130.28 132.08 133.12 138.20

(c) How does the shape of the graph of the span=10 smoother differ from that of the span=1 smoother?

[A] The span=10 smoother is always above the span=1 smoother.

[B] The span=10 smoother is always below the span=1 smoother.

[C] The span=10 smoother is straighter than the span=1 smoother.

EXERCISE 2

The cherry-tree data gives wood volume (in cubic feet) along with height (in feet) and girth (in inches — even though the name "Girth" is used, it's really a diameter).

Construct a smoother of two variables for the cherry data with span=1. (Warning: Be careful to match the capitalization of the names).

What's the value when height is 50 feet and "Girth" (that is, diameter) is 15 inches?

24.4 25.5 26.6 27.7 28.8

EXERCISE 3

The data set BodyFat.csv contains several body measurements made on a group of 252 men. You're going to look at theses variables:

- Weight — the total body weight in pounds.
- BodyFat — the percentage of total weight that is fat.
- Abdomen — the circumference at the waist in cm.

(a) Construct a smoother of BodyFat as a function of Weight with span=1.

    (i) What is the value of this function for Weight=150? 13.46 14.36 16.34

    (ii) What's the general shape of the function?

        A Sloping up and curved downwards

        B Sloping down and curved upwards

        C Straight line sloping downwards

(b) Construct a smoother of BodyFat as a function of Abdomen with span=1.

    (i) What is the value of this function for Abdomen=100?

23.34 23.85 24.43 25.23 26.74 27.25

    (ii) What's the general shape of the function?

        A Sloping up and curved downwards

        B Sloping down and curved upwards

        C Straight line sloping downwards

(c) Construct a smoother of BodyFat as a function of both Abdomen and Weight with span=1. What is the value of this function for Abdomen=100 and Weight=150?

23.34 23.85 24.43 25.23 26.74 27.25

Make a contour plot of your smoother function. Using the plot, answer this question: How does body fat percentage change when increasing weight from 140 to 240 pounds, but holding abdominal circumference constant at 90cm?

    A Body fat percentage doesn't change on weight.

    B Body fat percentage goes down with increasing weight.

    C Body fat percentage goes up with increasing weight.

3. Fitting Functions to Data

Often, you have an idea for the form of a function for a model and you need to select parameters that will make the model function a good match for observations. The process of selecting parameters to match observations is called **model fitting**.

To illustrate, the data in the file `"utilities.csv"` records the average temperature each month (in degrees F) as well as the monthly natural gas usage (in cubic feet, ccf). There is, as you might expect, a strong relationship between the two.

```
u = fetchData("utilities.csv")
plotPoints(ccf ~ temp, data=u)
```

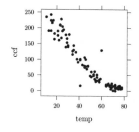

Many different sorts of functions might be used to represent these data. One of the simplest and most commonly used in modeling is a straight-line function $f(x) = Ax + B$. In function $f(x)$, the variable x stands for the input, while A and B are parameters. It's important to remember what are the names of the inputs and outputs when fitting models to data — you need to arrange for the name to match the corresponding data.

With the utilities data, the input is the temperature, `temp`. The output that is to be modeled is `ccf`. To fit the model function to the data, you write down the formula with the appropriate names of inputs, parameters, and the output in the right places:

```
f = fitModel(ccf ~ A*temp + B, data=u)
```

The output of `fitModel()` is a function of the same form as you specified with specific numerical values given to the parameters in order to make the function best match the data.

The point of the fitting process is to find the coefficients that bring the function as close as possible to the data. You can easily see the coefficients that are found by fitting by applying the coef() operator to the model.

```
coef(f)

      A       B
 -3.464 253.098
```

Most often, you will be interested in the function itself, for example to graph it along with the data.

```
plotFun( f(temp)~temp, temp.lim=range(0,80))
plotPoints(ccf ~ temp, data=u, add=TRUE)
```

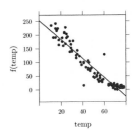

You can add other functions into the mix easily. For instance, you might think that sqrt(temp) works in there somehow. Try it out!

```
f2 = fitModel(ccf ~ A*temp + B + C*sqrt(temp),
              data=u)
plotFun( f2(temp)~temp, temp.lim = range(0,80))
plotPoints(ccf ~ temp, data=u, add=TRUE)
```

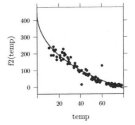

This example has involved just one input variable. Throughout the natural and social sciences, a very important and widely used technique is to use multiple variables as inputs. To illustrate, look at the data in "used-hondas.csv" on the prices of used Honda automobiles.

```
hondas = fetchData("used-hondas.csv")
head(hondas)

  Price Year Mileage Location Color Age
1 20746 2006   18394 St.Paul  Grey    1
2 19787 2007       8 St.Paul Black    0
3 17987 2005   39998 St.Paul  Grey    2
4 17588 2004   35882 St.Paul Black    3
5 16987 2004   25306 St.Paul  Grey    3
6 16987 2005   33399 St.Paul Black    2
```

As you can see, the dataset includes the variables Price, Age, and Mileage. It seems reasonable to think that price will depend both on the mileage and age of the car. Here's a very simple model that uses both variables:

```
carPrice1 = fitModel(
  Price ~ A + B*Age + C*Mileage,
  data=hondas)
```

You can plot that out as a mathematical function:

```
plotFun( carPrice1(Age=age, Mileage=miles)~age&miles,
         age.lim=range(2,8), miles.lim=range(0,60000))
```

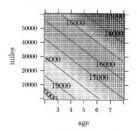

A somewhat more sophisticated model might include what's called an "interaction" between age and mileage, recognizing that the effect of age might be different depending on mileage.

```
carPrice2 = fitModel(Price ~ A+B*Age+C*Mileage+D*Age*Mileage,
                     data=hondas)
```

Again, once the function has been fitted, you can plot it in the ordinary way:

```
plotFun( carPrice2(Age=age, Mileage=miles)~age & miles,
         age.lim=range(0,10), miles.lim=range(0,100000))
```

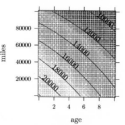

Notice that the price of a used car goes down with age and with mileage. This is hardly unexpected. The fitted model quantifies the relationship, and from the graph you can see that the effect of 2 years of age is roughly the same as 20,000 miles.

Each of the above models has involved what are called **linear parameters**. Often, there are parameters in functions that appear in a **nonlinear** way. Examples include k in $f(t) = A\exp(kt) + C$ and P in $A\sin(\frac{2\pi}{P}t) + C$. The idea of function fitting applies perfectly well to nonlinear parameters, but the task is harder for the computer. You'll get the best results if you give the computer a hint for the values of nonlinear parameters.

To illustrate, consider the `"Income-Housing.csv"` data which shows an exponential relationship between the fraction of families with two cars and income:

```
inc = fetchData("Income-Housing.csv")
plotPoints(TwoVehicles ~ Income, data=inc)
```

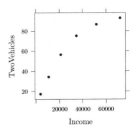

The pattern of the data suggests exponential "decay" towards close to 100% of the families having two vehicles. The mathematical form of this exponential function is $Aexp(-kY) + C$. A and C are unknown linear parameters. k is an unknown nonlinear parameter — it will be negative for exponential decay.

Suppose you make a guess at k. The guess doesn't need to be completely random; you can see from the data themselves that the "half-life" is something like $25,000. The parameter k is corresponds to the half life, $k = \ln(0.5)/\text{half-life}$, so a good guess for k is $\ln(0.5)/25000$, that is

```
kguess = log(0.5)/25000
kguess
```

```
[1] -2.773e-05
```

It's also helpful to have reasonable guesses for the other parameters. You can make reasonable estimates from the graph. A corresponds to the "leveling-off" value of the function, which is around 100. B is negative and about the same size as A (since essentially nobody has two vehicles for a family income of 0). Starting with those guesses, fitModel() can find good-fitting values for the parameters:

```
f = fitModel( TwoVehicles ~ A + B*exp(k*Income), data=inc,
                    start=list(A=100,B=-100,k=log(0.5)/25000))
```

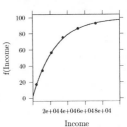

```
plotFun(f(Income)~Income, Income.lim=range(0,100000))
plotPoints(TwoVehicles ~ Income, data=inc, add=TRUE)
```

The graph goes satisfyingly close to the data points. But you can also look at the numerical values of the function for any income:

```
f(Income=10000)
```

```
[1] 33.78
```

```
f(Income=50000)
```

```
[1] 85.44
```

It's particularly informative to look at the values of the function for the specific Income levels in the data used for fitting, that is, the dataset inc:

```
f(Income=inc$Income)
```

```
[1] 16.38 35.82 56.67 74.01 86.45 93.48
```

The residuals are the difference between these model values and the actual values of TwoVehicles in the dataset:

```
resids = inc$TwoVehicles - f(Income=inc$Income)
resids
```

```
[1]   0.9247 -1.5186 -0.2713  1.2948  0.1478 -0.5774
```

This set of numbers is a vector; its length tells how "far" the function is from the data. Recall that the square-length of a vector is the sum of squared residuals

```
sum(resids^2)
```

```
[1] 5.267
```

The "distance" — or rather the square distance — between the function and the data is the sum of square residuals.

Keep in mind that the sum of square residuals is a function of the parameters. The parameters are being chosen by fitModel() in order to make the sum of square residuals as small as possible, in other words, to fit the function to the data.

EXAMPLE: The cooling of a hot object to the ambient temperature is generally modeled by an exponential process. Let's see. The data "stan-data.csv" contain temperature measurements of a cup of hot water as it cools to room temperature. To fit an exponential decay model, $T = A + Be^{-kt}$, we'll need an estimate for the nonlinear parameter k. Looking at a plot of the data

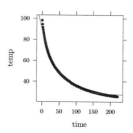

Figure 10: The temperature of cooling water and a fitted exponential model.

suggests that it takes about 50 seconds for the initial temperature to fall by about half of its eventual total fall. This suggests $k = \ln(2)/50$.

```
water = fetchData("stan-data.csv")
plotPoints(temp~time, data=water)
f = fitModel(temp ~ A + B*exp(-k*time), data=water,
             start=list(k=log(2)/50))
plotFun( f(time)~time, add=TRUE, col="red")
```

You can see from the plot that the model captures the gross shape of the data, but deviates from it at the start and at the end. It's helpful to plot out the residuals — the data values minus their corresponding model values.

```
plotPoints( temp - f(time) ~ time, data=water)
```

Ideally, these should be near zero and show no particular pattern in their deviations from zero. As you can see, however, these residuals show systematic trends: slow oscillations above and below zero. That indicates that the model is not representing the cooling process very well. It turns out that there are at least two cooling processes, water to mug and water to air. A model with two exponentials, one fast and one slow, does a much better job.

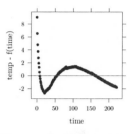

Figure 11: Residuals from the model show systematic trends around zero.

Exercises

EXERCISE 1 The data in `"stan-data.csv"` contains measurements made by Prof. Stan Wagon of the temperature of a cooling cup of hot water. The variables are `temp` and `time`: temperature in degrees C and time in minutes.

Find the best value of k in the exponential model $A + B\exp(kt)$.

(a) What's the value of k that gives the smallest sum of square residuals? (Pick the closest one.)

    -2.00 -0.20 -0.02 -0.002 -0.0002

(b) What are the units of this k? (This is not an R question, but a mathematical one.)

    $\boxed{A}$ seconds
    $\boxed{B}$ minutes
    $\boxed{C}$ per second
    $\boxed{D}$ per minute

EXERCISE 2 The `"hawaii.csv"` dataset contains a record of ocean tide levels in Hawaii over a few days. The `time` variable is in hours. You are going to fit the function $f(t) = A\sin\left(\frac{2\pi}{P}(t - T_0)\right) + C$. Since the tides occur with a period of roughly 1 day, a good guess for a starting value of P is 24 hours.

```
hawaii = fetchData("hawaii.csv")
f=fitModel(water~A*sin(2*pi*(time-T0)/P)+C,
        start=list(P=24,T0=0), data=hawaii)
```

(a) What is the period P (in hours) that makes the sum of square residuals error as small as possible?

    23.42 24.00 24.28 24.54 24.78 25.17

(b) Plot out the data and the fitted function. You may notice that the "best fitting" sine wave is not particularly close to the data points. One reason for this is that the pattern is more complicated than a simple sine wave. You can get a better approximation by including additional sine functions with a period of $2P$. (This is called a harmonic.) Overall, the model function will be:

$$f2(t) = \quad A \;\; \sin\left(\frac{2\pi}{P}(t - T_0)\right) + $$
$$B \;\; \sin\left(\frac{2\pi}{P/2}(t - T_1)\right) + C.$$

What period P (in hours) shows up as best when you add in a harmonic to the model?

    23.42 24.00 24.28 24.54 24.78 25.17

A more complete model of tides includes multiple periods stemming from the multiple factors involved: the earth's rotation, the moon's revolution around the earth, the alignment of the moon and the sun, etc.

4. Solving

4.1 Solving Equations

Many of high-school algebra involves "solving." In the typical, textbook situation, you have an equation, say

$$3x + 2 = y$$

and you are asked to "solve" the equation for x. This involves rearranging the symbols of the equation in the familiar ways, e.g., moving the 2 to the right hand side and dividing by the 3. These steps, originally termed "balancing" and "reduction" are summarized in the original meaning of the arabic word "al-jabr"[3] used by Muhammad ibn Musa al-Khowarizmi (c. 780-850) in his "*Compendious Book on Calculation by Completion and Balancing*". This is where our word "algebra" originates.

High school students are also taught a variety of *ad hoc* techniques for solving in particular situations. For example, the quadratic equation $ax^2 + bx + c = 0$ can be solved by application of the procedures of "factoring," or "completing the square," or use of the quadratic formula:

$$x = \frac{-b \pm \sqrt{b^2 - 4ac}}{2a}.$$

Parts of this formula can be traced back to at least the year 628 in the writings of Brahmagupta, an Indian mathematician, but the complete formula seems to date from Simon Stevin in Europe in 1594 and was published by René Descartes in 1637.

For some problems, students are taught named operations that involve the inverse of functions. For instance, to solve $\sin(x) = y$, one simply writes down

$x = \arcsin(y)$ without any detail on how to find arcsin beyond "use a calculator" or, in the old days, "use a table from a book."

From Equations to Zeros of Functions

With all of this emphasis on procedures such as factoring and moving symbols back and forth around an = sign, students naturally ask, "How do I solve equations in R?"

The answer is surprisingly simple, but to understand it, you need to have a different perspective on what it means to "solve" and where the concept of "equation" comes in.

The general form of the problem that is typically used in numerical calculations on the computer is that the equation to be solved is really a function to be inverted. That is, for numerical computation, the problem should be stated like this:

You have a function $f(x)$. You happen to know the form of the function f and the value of the output y for some unknown input value x. Your task: find the input x that will produce output y.

One way to solve such problems is to find an expression for the **inverse of** f. The expression for the inverse can be difficult or impossible to derive, but the notion of the inverse function is simple. There's even a standard notation [4] to indicate the inverse of a function: f^{-1}. Fortunately, it's rarely necessary to find an expression for the inverse. Instead, the problem can be handled by finding the **zeros** of f.

If you can plot out the function $f(x)$ for a range of x, you can easily find the zeros. Just find where the x where the function crosses the y-axis. This works for any function, even ones that are so complicated that there aren't algebraic procedures for finding a solution.

To illustrate, consider the function

[4] Many students understandably but mistakenly take f^{-1} to mean $1/f(x)$. The first is a function inverse, the second is the value of the function divided into 1.

```
plotFun(sin(x^2)*cos(sqrt(x^4+3)-x^2)-x+1 ~ x,
        x.lim=range(-3,3))
```

You can see easily enough that the function crosses the y axis somewhere between $x = 1$ and $x = 2$. You can get

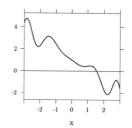

x

more detail by zooming in around the approximate solution:

```
plotFun(sin(x^2)*(cos(sqrt(x^4+3)-x^2))-x+1 ~ x,
        x.lim=range(1,2))
```

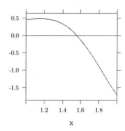

The crossing is at roughly $x \approx 1.6$. You could, of course, zoom in further to get a better approximation. Or, you can let the software do this for you:

```
findZeros(sin(x^2)*(cos(sqrt(x^4+3)-x^2))-x+1 ~ x,
          x.lim=range(1,2))
```

```
      x
1 1.558
```

The syntax of findZeros() is very much like plotFun(), but now the argument x.lim is used to state where to look for a solution.

You need only have a rough idea of where the solution is. For example:

```
findZeros(sin(x^2)*(cos(sqrt(x^4+3)-x^2))-x+1 ~ x,
          x.lim=range(-1000,1000))
```

```
      x
1 1.558
```

You can even say, "I have no idea at all," by telling the software to look anywhere between $-\infty$ and ∞.

```
findZeros(sin(x^2)*(cos(sqrt(x^4+3)-x^2))-x+1 ~ x,
          x.lim=range(-Inf,Inf))
```

```
      x
1 1.558
```

The findZeros() function will never look outside the interval you specify. It will do a more precise job within the interval if you can state the interval in a narrow way.

Setting up a Problem

As the name suggests, findZeros() finds the zeros of functions. You can set up any solution problem in this form. For example, suppose you want to solve $e^{kt} = 2^{bt}$ for b, knowing k, for example, $k = 0.00035$. You may, of course, remember how to do this problem using logarithms. But here's the set up for findZeros():

```
findZeros( exp(k*t) - 2^(b*t) ~ b, k=0.00035, t=1,
          b.lim=range(-Inf,Inf) )

        b
1 5e-04
```

Note that the "I have no idea" interval of $-\infty$ to ∞ was used. You're usually better off if you have a finite interval in mind, which you can set *after* you get a rough idea of the solution:

```
findZeros( exp(k*t) - 2^(b*t) ~ b, k=0.00035, t=1,
          b.lim=range(0,0.001) )

        b
1 5e-04
```

Multiple Solutions

The findZeros() function will try to find multiple solutions if they exist. For instance, the equation $\sin(x) = 0.35$ has an infinite number of solutions. Here are some of them:

```
findZeros( sin(x)-0.35 ~ x, x.lim=range(-10,10) )

          x
1 -12.2088
2  -9.7824
3  -5.9256
4  -3.4992
5   0.3576
6   2.7840
7   6.6408
8   9.0672
```

Exercises

PROBLEM 1
Solve the equation
$\sin(\cos(x^2) - x) - x = 0.5$ for x.
  0.0000 0.1328 0.2098 0.3654 0.4217

PROBLEM 2
Find any zeros of the function
$3e^{-t/5}\sin\left(\frac{2\pi}{2}t\right)$ that are between $t = 1$ and $t = 10$.

[A] There aren't any zeros in that interval.

[B] There aren't any zeros at all!

[C] $2, 4, 6, 8$

[D] $1, 3, 5, 7, 9$

[E] $1, 2, 3, 4, 5, 6, 7, 8, 9$

PROBLEM 3
Use findZeros() to find the zeros of each of these polynomials:

(a) $3x^2 + 7x - 10$

[A] $x = -3.33$ or 1

[B] $x = 3.33$ or 1

[C] $x = -3.33$ or -1

[D] $x = 3.33$ or -1

[E] No zeros

(b) $4x^2 - 2x + 20$

[A] $x = -3.33$ or 1

[B] $x = 3.33$ or 1

[C] $x = -3.33$ or -1

[D] $x = 3.33$ or -1

[E] No zeros

(c) $2x^3 - 4x^2 - 3x - 10$
Which one of these is a zero?
  -1.0627 0 1.5432 1.8011 2.1223 3.0363 none

(d) $7x^4 - 2x^3 - 4x^2 - 3x - 10$
Which one of these is a zero?
  -1.0627 0 1.5432 1.8011 2.1223 3.0363 none

(e) $6x^5 - 7x^4 - 2x^3 - 4x^2 - 3x - 10$
Which one of these is a zero?
  -1.0627 0 1.5432 1.8011 2.1223 3.0363 none

EXERCISE 4
Construct a smoother for the height of pine trees as a function of age:

```
pine = fetchData("Loblolly")
heightfun = spliner(height ~ age, data=pine)
```

Use findZeros() to find the age at which the height will be 35 feet.
  11.3 11.9 12.2 12.7 13.1

4.2 Linear Algebra and Projection

Linear algebra operations are among the most important in science and technology:

- Project a single vector onto the space defined by a set of vectors.

- Match a given vector with a linear combination of other vectors.

In performing these operations, you will use two main functions, project() and mat(), along with the ordinary multiplication * and addition + operations. There is also a new sort of operation that provides a compact description for taking a linear combination: "matrix multiplication," written %*%.

To start, consider the sort of linear algebra problem often presented in textbooks in the form of simultaneous linear equations. For example:

$$
\begin{array}{rcrcl}
x & + & 5y & = & 1 \\
2x & + & -2y & = & 1 \\
4x & + & 0y & = & 1
\end{array}
$$

Many people will think of the above as a system of three simultaneous equations. Another perspective is valuable, however: treat the system as a single equation involving vector quantities. To highlight the vectors, re-write the equation like this:

$$
x \begin{pmatrix} 1 \\ 2 \\ 4 \end{pmatrix} + y \begin{pmatrix} 5 \\ -2 \\ 0 \end{pmatrix} = \begin{pmatrix} 1 \\ 1 \\ 1 \end{pmatrix}.
$$

Solving this vector equation involves **projecting** the vector $\vec{b} = \begin{pmatrix} 1 \\ 1 \\ 1 \end{pmatrix}$ onto the space defined by the two vectors $\vec{v}_1 = \begin{pmatrix} 1 \\ 2 \\ 4 \end{pmatrix}$ and $\vec{v}_2 = \begin{pmatrix} 5 \\ -2 \\ 0 \end{pmatrix}$. The solution, x and y will be the number of multiples of their respective vectors needed to reach the projected vectors.

A linear combination means to scale and add up vectors. The matching problem consists of finding the correct scales so that the sum equals the given vector. Projecting a vector onto a space is analogous to seeing where the shadow of an object will fall. It means to find the point in the space that is closest to the vector.

When setting this up with the R notation that you will be using, you need to create each of the vectors $\vec{b}, \vec{v}_1$, and $\vec{v}_2$. Here's how:

```
b = c(1,1,1)
v1 = c(1,2,4)
v2 = c(5,-2,0)
```

The projection is accomplished using the `project()` function:

```
project(b ~ v1 + v2)

       [,1]
v1 0.32895
v2 0.09211
```

Read this as "project $\vec{b}$ onto the subspace defined by $\vec{v}_1$ and $\vec{v}_1$.

The output is given in the form of the multiplier on $\vec{v}_1$ and $\vec{v}_2$, that is, the values of x and y in the original problem. This answer is the "best" in the sense that these particular values for x and y are the ones that come the closest to $\vec{b}$, that is, the linear combination that give the projection of $\vec{b}$ onto the subspace defined by $\vec{v}_1$ and $\vec{v}_2$.

If you want to see what that projection is, just multiply the coefficients by the vectors and add them up. In other words, take the linear combination

```
0.32894737*v1 + 0.09210526*v2

[1] 0.7895 0.4737 1.3158
```

NOTICE THAT THE PROJECTED VALUE IS NOT EXACTLY the same as $\vec{b}$, even though it is the linear combination of $\vec{v}_1$ and $\vec{v}_2$ that reaches as close to $\vec{b}$ as possible, in other words the projection of $\vec{b}$ onto the subspace spanned by $\vec{v}_1$ and $\vec{v}_2$. The difference between $\vec{b}$ and it's projection is called the **residual**. The residual is also a vector and can be calculated by subtracting the projection from $\vec{b}$:

```
b - (0.32894737*v1 + 0.09210526*v2)

[1]   0.2105   0.5263  -0.3158
```

Matrices: Collections of Vectors

When there are lots of vectors involved in the linear combination, it's easier to be able to refer to all of them by a single object name. The mat() function takes the vectors and packages them together into a matrix. It works just like project(), but doesn't involve the vector that's being projected onto the subspace. Like this:

```
A = mat( ~ v1 + v2)
A

      v1 v2
[1,]   1  5
[2,]   2 -2
[3,]   4  0
```

Notice that A doesn't have any new information; it's just the two vectors $\vec{v}_1$ and $\vec{v}_2$ placed side by side.

Here's the same projection, but using $\vec{v}_1$ and $\vec{v}_2$ packaged up together in **A**:

```
x = project( b ~ A)
x

        [,1]
Av1 0.32895
Av2 0.09211
```

To get the linear combination of the vectors in A, you matrix-multiply the matrix A times the solution x. The odd-looking %*% operator invokes matrix multiplication.

```
A %*% x

        [,1]
[1,] 0.7895
[2,] 0.4737
[3,] 1.3158
```

The output from the matrix multiplication is, of course, the same answer you got when you did the vector-wise multiplication "by hand."

The "Intercept"

Very often, your projections will involve a vector of all 1s. This vector is so common that it has a name, the "intercept." There is even a special notation for the intercept in the mat() and project() functions: +1. For instance:

```
A = mat( ~ v1 + v2 + 1)
A
```

```
     (Intercept) v1 v2
[1,]          1  1  5
[2,]          1  2 -2
[3,]          1  4  0
```

Redundancy and the "best" solution

The instruction to "project" is implicit in traditional linear algebraic notation. Rather than an imperative command to do something, the traditional notation writes out the relationship, e.g. $\mathbf{A} \cdot \vec{x} = \vec{b}$, and leaves it to the human reader to determine what quantities are unknown and what operation is appropriate to find the unknown quantities. For instance, if you know $\mathbf{A}$ and $\vec{x}$, then finding the unknown $\vec{b}$ in $\mathbf{A} \cdot \vec{x} = \vec{b}$ means performing matrix multiplication A %*% x.

When, as in the example introducing this chapter, it's $\vec{x}$ that's unknown, it often happens that that there is no exact solution or that there is no unique solution. The method used by project() looks for a "best" solution in such cases. The appropriate meaning of "best" can depend on the purposes for which the unknown is being sought.

Part of the definition of "best" that's implicit in the solution method used by project() is to make the residual vector as small as possible: the so-called

least-squares solution. This is usually the standard and appropriate thing to do.

Another aspect of "best" that's not so standard has to do with handling cases where the vectors on the right-hand side of ~ are **linearly dependent**, that is, where there are more vectors than strictly needed to define a unique subspace. As a simple example, consider this projection problem:

```
b = c(3,5,-1)
v1 = c(1,2,3)
v2 = c(2,4,6)
```

The vectors v1 and v2 point in the same direction. That is, even though there are two vectors v1 and v2, the two vectors define a subspace that is only one dimensional.

The project() method of solution handles this redundancy by involving both vectors in the linear combination:

```
project(b~v1+v2)

         [,1]
v1 0.1429
v2 0.2857
```

Another possible choice, commonly used in statistics, is to consider the minimal set of vectors that define the subspace and to exclude the other vectors from the projection.

Functions from Fitting

Often, model functions are created by fitting a linear combination of simple functions to data. The coefficients of such a fitted linear combination can be calculated using project().

Sometimes it's convenient to package up the results of a fit as a function rather than a vector of coefficients. To illustrate, consider the data contained in the "cardata.csv" file giving measurements on various 1978-79 model cars:

The statistical convention is implemented by the lm() operator which works much like project(). In addition to excluding redundant vectors, lm() includes an intercept vector unless explicitly forbidden to do so by a -1 term, as in this projection of $\vec{b}$ onto $\vec{v}_1$ and $\vec{v}_2$:

```
lm(b~v1+v2-1)


     v1      v2
0.7143      NA
```

The exclusion of a redundant vector is signalled by returning NA as its coefficient in the linear combination.

The outputs from project() and from lm() are equivalent: they imply exactly the same location for the projection of $\vec{b}$, but the statistical method is more "compact" in that it involves fewer vectors in the linear combination.

```
cars = fetchData("cardata.csv")
```

	mpg	pounds	horsepower	cylinders	tons
1	16.9	3968	155	8	2.0
2	15.5	3689	142	8	1.8
3	19.2	3281	125	8	1.6
4	18.5	3585	150	8	1.8
5	30.0	1961	68	4	1.0
6	27.5	2330	95	4	1.2

Figure 12: Some of the data on car size, power, and mileage from "cardata.csv"

Suppose you want to construct a model function that relates miles-per-gallon to the weight and horsepower of the cars. You can, of course, use project():

```
project(mpg ~1+pounds+horsepower, data=cars)

                    [,1]
(Intercept)  46.932738
pounds       -0.002902
horsepower   -0.144931
```

The result is a vector of coefficients.

Compare the behavior of project() to that of fitModel(). Whereas project() returns a vector of coefficients, fitModel() gives back a function with named parameters. The two are, of course, closely related. For example:

```
fmpg = fitModel(mpg~A+B*pounds+C*horsepower, data=cars)
coef(fmpg)

        A          B          C
46.932745  -0.002902  -0.144931
```

You may wonder, why use project, which works only for linear parameters, when fitModel can handle both linear parameters and nonlinear parameters. Unfortunately, the mathematics of nonlinear fitting is more difficult than that of linear algebra. This shows up by the need to give initial guesses for the parameters in fitModel, both linear and nonlinear. In contrast, the linear algebra methods are simpler and do not require any initial guess for the linear parameters. In addition, models with only linear parameters are generally easier to interpret and often provide a satisfactory representation of the pattern seen in data. As such, it's very common to use linear models even if a nonlinear model fits somewhat better. There is even an intermediate sort of method, called **generalized linear models** (GLM) that provides much of the benefit of linear models and much of the flexibility of nonlinear models. Perhaps the most commonly used GLM is called **logistic regression**.

Exercises

EXERCISE 1
  Remember all those "find the line that goes through the points problems" from algebra class. They can be a bit simpler with the proper linear-algebra tools.
  Example: "Find the line that goes through the points $(2, 3)$ and $(7, -8)$."
  One way to interpret this is that we are looking for a relationship between x and y such that $y = mx + b$. In vector terms, this means that the x-coordinates of the two points, 2 and 7, made into a vector $\begin{pmatrix} 2 \\ 7 \end{pmatrix}$ will be scaled by m, and an intercept vector $\begin{pmatrix} 1 \\ 1 \end{pmatrix}$ will be scaled by b.

```
x = c(2,7)
y = c(3,-8)
project(y ~ x + 1)
              [,1]
(Intercept)   7.4
x            -2.2
```

  Now you know m and b.

YOUR TASK: Using the `project()` function:

(a) Find the line that goes through the two points $(9, 1)$ and $(3, 7)$.

  A $y = x + 2$
  B $y = -x + 10$
  C $y = x + 0$
  D $y = -x + 0$
  E $y = x - 2$

(b) Find the line that goes through the origin $(0, 0)$ and $(2, -2)$.

  A $y = x + 2$
  B $y = -x + 10$
  C $y = x + 0$
  D $y = -x + 0$
  E $y = x - 2$

(c) Find the line that goes through $(1, 3)$ and $(7, 9)$.

  A $y = x + 2$
  B $y = -x + 10$
  C $y = x + 0$
  D $y = -x + 0$
  E $y = x - 2$

EXERCISE 2

(a) Find x, y, and z that solve the following:

$$x \begin{pmatrix} 1 \\ 2 \\ 4 \end{pmatrix} + y \begin{pmatrix} 5 \\ -2 \\ 0 \end{pmatrix} + z \begin{pmatrix} 1 \\ -2 \\ 3 \end{pmatrix} = \begin{pmatrix} 1 \\ 1 \\ 1 \end{pmatrix}.$$

What's the value of x?

-0.2353 0.1617 0.4264 1.3235 1.5739

(b) Find x, y, and z that solve the following:

$$x \begin{pmatrix} 1 \\ 2 \\ 4 \end{pmatrix} + y \begin{pmatrix} 5 \\ -2 \\ 0 \end{pmatrix} + z \begin{pmatrix} 1 \\ -2 \\ 3 \end{pmatrix} = \begin{pmatrix} 1 \\ 4 \\ 3 \end{pmatrix}.$$

What's the value of x?

-0.2353 0.1617 0.4264 1.3235 1.5739

EXERCISE 3

Using project(), solve these sets of simultaneous linear equations for x, y, and z:

1. Two equations in two unknowns:

$$\begin{aligned} x + 2y &= 1 \\ 3x + 2y &= 7 \end{aligned}$$

A $x = 3$ and $y = -1$
B $x = 1$ and $y = 3$
C $x = 3$ and $y = 3$

2. Three equations in three unknowns:

$$\begin{aligned} x + 2y + 7z &= 1 \\ 3x + 2y + 2z &= 7 \\ -2x + 3y + z &= 7 \end{aligned}$$

A $x = 3.1644, y = -0.8767, z = 0.8082$
B $x = -0.8767, y = 0.8082, z = 3.1644$
C $x = 0.8082, y = 3.1644, z = -0.8767$

3. Four equations in four unknowns:

$$\begin{aligned} x + 2y + 7z + 8w &= 1 \\ 3x + 2y + 2z + 2w &= 7 \\ -2x + 3y + z + w &= 7 \\ x + 5y + 3z + w &= 3 \end{aligned}$$

A $x = 5.500, y = -7.356, z = 3.6918, w = 1.1096$
B $x = 1.1096, y = 3.6918, z = -7.356, w = 5.500$
C $x = 5.500, y = -7.356, z = 1.1096, w = 3.6918$
D $x = 1.1096, y = -7.356, z = 5.500, w = 3.6918$

4. Three equations in four unknowns:

$$\begin{aligned} x + 2y + 7z + 8w &= 1 \\ 3x + 2y + 2z + 2w &= 7 \\ -2x + 3y + z + w &= 7 \end{aligned}$$

TRUE or FALSE There is an exact solution. (Hint: What's the residual?)

5. Derivatives & Differentiation

The operator for taking derivatives is D(). Like all ooperators, D() takes inputs and produces an output. D() is quite simple: it takes just one input.

- Input: an expression using the ~ notation. Examples:

  x^2~x   sin(x^2)   y*cos(x)~y

On the left of the ~ is a mathematical expression written in correct R notation that will evaluate to a number when numerical values are available for all of the quantities referenced. On the right of the ~ is the variable with respect to which the derivative is to be taken. By no means need this be called x or y; any valid variable name is allowed.

The output produced by D() is a function. The function will list as arguments all of the variables contained in the input expression. You can then evaluate the output function for particular numerical values of the arguments in order to find the value of the derivative function.

For example:

g = **D**(x^2 ~ x)   **g**(1)   **g**(3.5)

                        [1] 2   [1] 7

Formulas and Numerical Difference. When the expression is relatively simple and composed of basic mathematical functions, D() will often return a function that contains a mathematical formula. For instance, in the above example

```
g
function (x)
2 * x
```

For other input expressions, D() will return a function
that is based on a numerical approximation to the
derivative — you can't "see" the derivative, but it is there
inside the numerical approximation method:

```
h = D( sin( abs(x-3) ) ~ x )
h

function (x)
numerical.first.partial(.function, .wrt, .hstep, match.call())
<environment: 0x1035a86a8>
```

Symbolic Parameters. You can include symbolic
parameters in an expression being input to D(), for
example:

```
s2 = D( A*sin(2*pi*t/P) + C ~ t)
```

The s2( ) function thus created will work like any
other mathematical function, but you will need to specify
numerical values for the symbolic parameters when you
evaluate the function:

```
s2

function (t, A, P, C)
A * (cos(2 * pi * t/P) * (2 * pi/P))

s2( t=3, A=2, P=10, C=4 )

[1] -0.3883

plotFun( s2(t,A=2,P=10,C=4) ~ t, t.lim=range(0,20))
```

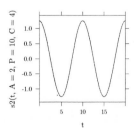

Partial Derivatives. The derivatives computed by D() are
partial derivatives. That is, they are derivatives where the
variable on the right-hand side of ~ is changed and all
other variables are held constant.

Second Derivatives. A second derivative is merely the derivative of a derivative. second derivatives You can use the D() operator twice to find a second derivative, like this.

```
df = D( sin(x) ~ x )
ddf = D( df(x) ~ x )
```

To save typing, particularly when there is more than one variable involved in the expression, you can put multiple variables to the right of the ~ sign, as in this second derivative with respect to *x*:

```
another.ddf = D( sin(x) ~ x & x )
```

This form for second and higher-order derivatives also delivers more accurate computations.

Exercises

EXERCISE 1

Using D(), find the derivative of
3*x^2 - 2*x + 4 ~ x.

(a) What is the value of the derivative at
$x = 0$? -6 -4 -3 -2 0 2 3 4 6

(b) What does a graph of the derivative
function look like?

    A A negative sloping line
    B A positive sloping line
    C An upward-facing parabola
    D A downward-facing parabola

EXERCISE 2

Using D(), find the derivative of
5*exp(.2*x) ~ x.

(a) What is the value of the derivative at
$x = 0$?
-5 -2 -1 0 1 2 5 .

(b) Plot out both the original exponential
expression and its derivative. How are
they related to each other?

    A They are the same function
    B Same exponential shape, but
different initial values
    C The derivative has a faster
exponential increase
    D The derivative shows an expo-
nential decay

EXERCISE 3

Use D() to find the derivative of e^{-x^2}
with respect to x (that is, exp(-(x^2) ~ x).
Graph the derivative from $x = -2$ to 2. What
does the graph look like?

    A A bell-shaped mountain
    B Exponential growth
    C A positive wave followed by a
negative wave
    D A negative wave followed by a
positive wave

EXERCISE 4 What will be the value of this
derivative?

D(fred^2 ~ ginger)

    A 0 everywhere
    B 1 everywhere
    C A positive sloping line
    D A negative sloping line

EXERCISE 5

Use D() to find the 3rd derivative of
cos(2*t). If you do this by using the ~t&t&t
notation, you will be able to read off a
formula for the 3rd derivative. What is it?

    A $\sin(t)$
    B $\sin(2t)$
    C $4\sin(2t)$
    D $8\sin(2t)$
    E $16\sin(2t)$
        What's the 4th derivative?
    A $\cos(t)$
    B $\cos(2t)$
    C $4\cos(2t)$
    D $8\cos(2t)$
    E $16\cos(2t)$

EXERCISE 6

Compute and graph the 4th derivative of
cos(2*t^2)~t from $t = 0$ to 5. What does the
graph look like?

    A A constant
    B A cosine whose period de-
creases as t gets bigger
    C A cosine whose amplitude
increases and whose period
decreases as t gets bigger
    D A cosine whose amplitude
decreases and whose period
increases as t gets bigger

For cos(2*t^2)~t the fourth derivate is a
complicated-looking expression made up of
simpler expressions. What functions appear

in the complicated expression?

A sin and cos functions

B sos, squaring, multiplication and addition

C cos, sin, squaring, multiplication and addition

D log, cos, sin, squaring, multiplication and addition

EXERCISE 7

Consider the expression x*sin(y) involving variables x and y. Use D() to compute several derivative functions: the partial with respect to x, the partial with respect to y, the second partial derivative with respect to x, the second partial derivative with respect to y, and these two mixed partials:

```
pxy = D(x*sin(y) ~ x&y)
pyx = D(x*sin(y) ~ y&x)
```

Pick several (x, y) pairs and evaluate each of the derivative functions at them. Use the results to answer the following:

- The partials with respect to x and to y are identical. TRUE or FALSE

- The second partials with respect to x and to y are identical. TRUE or FALSE

- The two mixed partials are identical. That is, it doesn't matter whether you differentiate first with respect to x and then y, or vice versa. TRUE or FALSE

6. Integrals & Anti-Differentiation

You've already seen the D operator, which takes the derivative of functions. There's also an antiD operator, which, as the name suggests, "undoes" differentiation. For instance:

```
f = makeFun( x^2 ~ x )
```

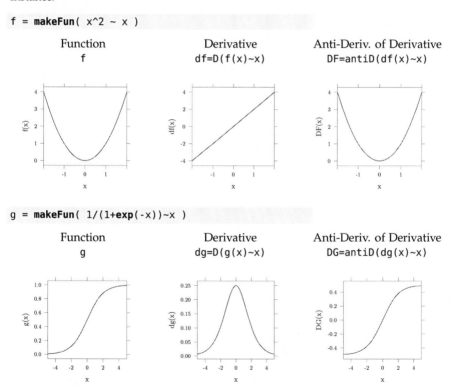

| Function
f | Derivative
df=D(f(x)~x) | Anti-Deriv. of Derivative
DF=antiD(df(x)~x) |

```
g = makeFun( 1/(1+exp(-x))~x )
```

| Function
g | Derivative
dg=D(g(x)~x) | Anti-Deriv. of Derivative
DG=antiD(dg(x)~x) |

You can apply anti-differentiation to any function, not just functions produced by differentiation. Indeed, it's rarely the case that you will want to anti-differentiate a function that you have just differentiated. One undoes the other, so there is little point except to illustrate how differentiation and anti-differentiation are related to one another. But it often happens that the information you have is a function that gives the derivative of some other function of interest.

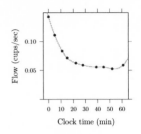

FOR EXAMPLE, consider how to measure the water lost in a leak from a pipe. It's easy to measure the flow from the leak; put a cup to catch the leaking fluid, then use a stopwatch to time how long it takes to fill up the cup. Imagine that you have done this occasionally and collected the following data over an hour:

Figure 13: The measured flow from the pipe.

time (min)	0	5	11	15	22	28	39	45	52	61
filltime (sec)	7	9	12	14	16	17	18	18	19	17

The flow rate has units of cups per second; you can calculate it as 1/FillTime. Evidently, the leak is slowing at first, then levels out, then seems to be increasing toward the end of the measurements.

You know the flow, but what is the total amount of water that has leaked. Among the possibilities:

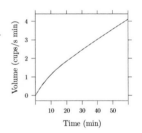

- Instead of a cup, put a bucket under the leak and catch all the water. Then you can measure how much is in the bucket.

- Use the anti-derivative of flow.

Figure 14: The accumulating volume of the leak.

Remember, flow is the time derivative of volume. Therefore, volume is the anti-derivative of flow with respect to time.

To construct the anti-derivative function, you first must put the derivative in the form of a function. A spline through the measurements seems suitable. (The data have been stored as `"startR/leak-example.csv"`.)

```
leakdata = fetchData("startR/leak-example.csv")
flow = spliner( 1/filltime ~ time, data=leakdata)
volume = antiD( flow(time)~time )
```

The anti-derivative function thus calculated, `volume`, is first and foremost a function of time. The derivative of the function is the `flow` function, which is why the slope of `volume` is steep at first and then climbs steadily.

Now suppose you wanted to know how much water has leaked during a particular interval of time, say from 10 minutes to 30 minutes. Easy. Put a empty bucket under the leak at time 10 minutes, then remove it at time 30 minutes and measure how much water has accumulated. Or, leave the bucket where it is, mark how much water is in the bucket at 10 minutes, record again at 30 minutes, and subtract. This second method is the strategy by which an anti-derivative function is used to find the accumulation:

```
volume(time=30)-volume(time=10)
```

[1] 1.335

Keep in mind that using the anti-derivative in this way to compute an integral, accomplishes the same thing you could do by accumulating the flow in a bucket, or multiplying the average flow by the duration.

Traditionally the definite integral is written like this (taking $f(t)$ to be the flow):

$$\int_{10}^{30} f(t)dt.$$

There is also a notation for an indefinite integral:

$$\int f(t)dt.$$

The two notations are very similar because the operations are closely related. But keep in mind that the two things are different.

The operation implied by writing the indefinite integral $\int f(t)dt$ is anti-differentiation: the construction of a new function. In the computer notation, constructing this function is done with `antiD`.

```
f = flow # Just renaming to match the traditional notation
F = antiD( f(t) ~ t)
```

(Traditionally, capital letters are used to denote the anti-derivative function.)

In interpreting this number, 1.335, it's important, as always, to take into account the units. The output of an anti-derivative function always has units that are the product of the units of the derivative function (cups/second in this example) and the variable of integration (minutes here). So the number is really 1.335 cup·minute/second. This may seem odd for a volume, but remember that 60 seconds equals a minute, so a minute/second is just 60 second/second is just 60. So the volume is $1.335 \times 60 = 80.1$ cups.

The operation implied by writing the definite integral $\int_{10}^{30} f(t)dt$ is implemented in three stages: construction of the anti-derivative function, evaluation of the anti-derivative function at the limits of integration, and then taking the difference between these values. Those last two stages are represented in this computer command.

```
F(30) - F(10)

[1] 1.335
```

Exercises

EXERCISE 1 Find the numerical value of each of the following definite integrals.

1. $\int_2^5 x^{1.5}dx$
   0.58 6.32 20.10 27.29 53.60 107.9 1486.8

2. $\int_0^{10} sin(x^2)dx$
   0.58 6.32 20.10 27.29 53.60 107.9 1486.8

3. $\int_1^4 e^{2x}dx$
   0.58 6.32 20.10 27.29 53.60 107.9 1486.8

4. $\int_{-2}^2 e^{2|x|}dx$
   0.58 6.32 20.10 27.29 53.60 107.9 1486.8

EXERCISE 2
There's a very simple relationship between $\int_a^b f(x)dx$ and $\int_b^a f(x)dx$ — integrating the same function f, but reversing the values of from and to. Create some functions, integrate them, and experiment with them to find the relationship.

[A] They are the same value.
[B] One is twice the value of the other.
[C] One is negative the other.
[D] One is the square of the other.

EXERCISE 3

The function being integrated can have additional variables or parameters beyond the variable of integration. To evaluate the definite integral, you need to specify values for those additional variables.

For example, a very important function in statistics and physics is the Gaussian, which has a bell-shaped graph:

```
gauss=makeFun((1/sqrt(2*pi*s^2))*exp(-(x-m)^2/(2*s^
   m=2,s=1.5)
plotFun(gauss(x)~x, x.lim=range(-10,10))
```

(You might want to cut-and-paste this definition of f() into your R session.) As you can see, it's a function of x, but also of the parameters mean and sigma.

Evaluate each of the following definite integrals:

1. $\int_0^1 gauss(x, m = 0, s = 1)dx$
   0.13 0.34 0.48 0.50 0.75 1.00

2. $\int_0^2 gauss(x, m = 0, s = 1)dx$

   <u>0.13</u> <u>0.34</u> <u>0.48</u> <u>0.50</u> <u>0.75</u> <u>1.00</u>

3. $\int_0^2 gauss(x, m = 0, s = 2)dx$

   <u>0.13</u> <u>0.34</u> <u>0.48</u> <u>0.50</u> <u>0.75</u> <u>1.00</u>

4. $\int_{-\infty}^3 gauss(x, m = 3, s = 10)dx$. (Hint: The mathematical $-\infty$ is represented as `-Inf` on the computer.)

   <u>0.13</u> <u>0.34</u> <u>0.48</u> <u>0.50</u> <u>0.75</u> <u>1.00</u>

5. $\int_{-\infty}^{\infty} gauss(x, m = 3, s = 10)dx$

   <u>0.13</u> <u>0.34</u> <u>0.48</u> <u>0.50</u> <u>0.75</u> <u>1.00</u>

7. Dynamics

One of the most useful applications for the calculus strategy involves studying how systems change in time: dynamics. Often, dynamics are described in terms of "differential equations." These relate the instantaneous state of a system $x(t)$ to the instantaneous change of state $\frac{dx}{dt}$. Solving — or "integrating" — a differential equation amounts to finding $x(t)$ given $\frac{dx}{dt}$.

As with other forms of integration, the setting is that you have information about the derivative of a function and want to deduce from this the function itself. When the information given is a function of the independent variable, for instance $\frac{dx}{dt} = f(t)$, then anti-differentiation can be used. But the usual setting for differential equations is that the derivative is known in terms of the state itself:

$$\frac{dx}{dt} = g(x).$$

The `integrateODE()` function solves such differential equations. In order to complete the solution, the starting, initial value of the state must be given.

To illustrate the difference between solving differential equations and finding anti-derivatives, consider these two different systems:

ANTI-DERIVATIVE: The derivative is known as a function of t.

$$\frac{dx}{dt} = f(t) = 1 - t.$$

To find the solution, use `antiD()` on $f(t)$:

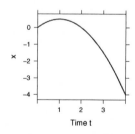

Figure 15: Solution to $\frac{dx}{dt} = 1 - t$

```
F = antiD( 1-t ~ t)
```

DIFFERENTIAL EQUATION: The derivative is known as a function of x.

$$\frac{dx}{dt} = g(x) = 1 - x.$$

To find the solution, use `integrateODE()` and specify how the change in the state x depends on x.

```
soln = integrateODE( dx ~ 1-x, x=0,
                tdur=list(from=0,to=4))
```

Note that it's necessary to give an initial condition for the state; the argument x=0 sets the initial condition to zero. You also have to specify the time interval over which the solution is to be found.

Although the two settings involve similar-looking formulas, they lead to completely different results.

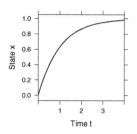

Figure 16: Solution to $\frac{dx}{dt} = 1 - x$ from initial condition $x = 0$

EXAMPLE: LOGISTIC GROWTH. The dynamical model for logistic growth involves a state x that grows at small values, but decays at large values:

$$\frac{dx}{dt} = rx(1 - x/K).$$

For $x < K$ the population grows while for $x > K$ the population decays. The state $x = K$ is a "stable equilibrium." It's an equilbrium because, when $x = K$, the change of state is nil: $dx/dt = 0$.

The `integrateODE()` function takes the differential equation as an input, together with the initial value of the state. Numerical values for all parameters must be specified, as they would in any case to draw a graph of the solution. In addition, must specify the range of time for which you want the function $x(t)$. For example, here's the solution for time running from 0 to 20.

```
soln <- integrateODE( dx ~ r*x*(1-x/K),
                x=1, K=10, r=.5,
                tdur=list(from=0,to=20))
```

The object that is created by `integrateODE()` is a function of time. Or, rather, it is a set of solutions, one for each of the state variables. In the logistic equation, there is only one state variable x. Finding the value of x at time

t means evaluating the function at some value of t. Here are the values at $t = 0, 1, \ldots, 5$:

```
soln$x(0:5)
```

```
[1] 1.000 1.548 2.320 3.324 4.509 5.751
```

Often, you will plot out the solution against time:

```
plotFun( soln$x(t)~t, t.lim=range(0,20))
```

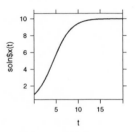

Figure 17: A solution to logistic-growth dynamics.

DIFFERENTIAL EQUATION SYSTEMS with more than one state variable can be handled as well. To illustrate, here is the SIR model of the spread of epidemics, in which the state is the number of susceptibles S and the number of infectives I in the population. Susceptibles become infective by meeting an infective, infectives recover and leave the system. There is one equation for the change in S and a corresponding equation for the change in I. The initial $I = 1$, corresponding to the start of the epidemic.

```
epi = integrateODE( dS~-a*S*I, dI~a*S*I - b*I,
  a=0.0026,b=.5,S=762,I=1,tdur=20)
```

This system of differential equations is solved to produce two functions, $S(t)$ and $I(t)$.

```
plotFun( epi$S(t)~t, t.lim=range(0,20))
plotFun( epi$I(t)~t, add=TRUE, col="red")
```

In the solution, you can see the epidemic grow to a peak near $t = 5$. At this point, the number of susceptibles has fallen so sharply that the number of infectives starts to fall as well. In the end, almost every susceptible has been infected.

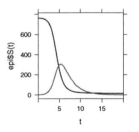

Figure 18: A solution $S(t)$ and $I(t)$ to the SIR dynamics.

THE PHASE PLANE provides a powerful format to visualize how the state of a two-variable system changes in time. Each point in the phase plane represents a state of the system. The dynamical rule — the differential equations — describe a flow field. The evolving state of the system is a trajectory that starts at an initial point and follows the flow.

The graphics for phase-plane display are best implemented using a graphical user interface. One such interface, is provided by the mPP() program (which works with RStudio). First, you must load the mPP software.

```
fetchData("mPP.R")
fetchData("DiffEQ.R")
```

Differential equations are specified using a function. For instance, the SIR equations can be implemented like this:

```
SIR = function(suscept,infective){
  a=0.0026; b=0.5
  dsuscept = -a*suscept*infective;
  dinfective = a*suscept*infective - b*infective;
  return( c(dsuscept, dinfective) );
}
```

To run the graphical user interface, call mPP():

```
mPP(DE=SIR, xlim=c(0,1000), ylim=c(-0,1000))
```

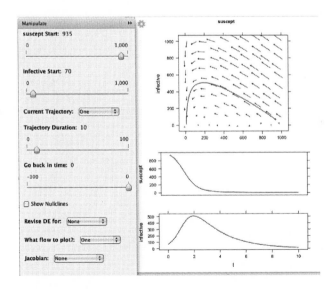

Figure 19: The mPP display with the SIR model.

EXAMPLE: ANOTHER DIVE FROM THE BOARD Consider a diver as she jumps off the high board and plunges into the water. You construct a dynamical model with state variables v and x: velocity and height.

```
dive = integrateODE( dv~-9.8, dx~v,
  v=1,x=5,tdur=1.2)
plotFun( dive$x(t)~t, t.lim=range(0,1.2))
```

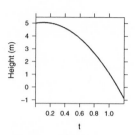

Figure 20: Diving without buoyancy or drag.

What's nice about the differential equation format is that it's easy to add features like the buoyancy of water and drag of the water. We'll do that here by changing the acceleration (the dv term) so that when $x < 0$ the acceleration is slightly positive with a drag term proportional to v^2 in the direction opposed to the motion.

```
diveFloat = integrateODE(
  dv~ifelse( h>0, -9.8, 1-sign(v)*v^2), dh~v,
  v=1,h=5,tdur=10)
plotFun( diveFloat$h(t)~t, t.lim=range(0,10))
```

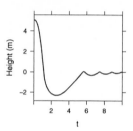

Figure 21: Buoyancy returns the diver to the surface, drag damps out the oscillations.

According to the model, the diver resurfaces after slightly more than 5 seconds, and then bobs in the water.

Exercises

EXERCISE 1 Use integrateODE() to find a solution to $\frac{dx}{dt} = 0.3x$ with initial condition $x = 2$. Find the solution value at time $t = 10$.

EXERCISE 2 Consider the SIR dynamics

```
epi=integrateODE(dS~ -a*S*I, dI~a*S*I-b*I,
  a=0.0026,b=.5,S=762,I=1,tdur=20)
```

1. Instead of starting with 1 infective (I=1), there are 10 infectives. Find the peak number of infectives as the epidemic plays out.
2. The parameter a corresponds to the rate

of transmission. Suppose you could half the rate of transmission, by, say, closing schools. What happens to the peak number of infectives?

EXERCISE 3 A simple model for the principal P of a home mortgage at 5% annual interest is $\frac{dP}{dt} = 0.05P - 10000$ where the annual payment is on the mortgage is $10000 and t is in years. Starting from an initial value of $P = 100000$, find the time at which the mortgage value goes to zero.

Activities

Activity 1: Where is the landscape the steepest?

You're going to create a terrain that you can examine visually. Your goal is to calculate where the terrain is steepest.

1. Create a function representing the height H of a terrain and plot it out in contour form. By changing the seed, you can create your own terrain.

```
H = rfun(~x&y, seed=677)
plotFun(H(x=x,y=y)~x&y,
        x.lim=range(-5,5),y.lim=range(-5,5))
```

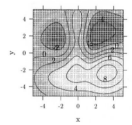

2. The partial derivatives reflect the slope of the terrain in the cardinal directions along the axes. You can calculate each of the partials $\partial H/\partial x$ and $\partial H/\partial y$. For example

```
dHdx = D(H(x=x,y=y)~x)
```

3. Plot out $\partial H/\partial x$ as a function of x and y.

```
plotFun(dHdx(x=x,y=y)~x&y,
        x.lim=range(-5,5),y.lim=range(-5,5))
```

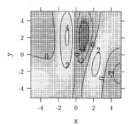

4. "Steepness" can be either uphill or downhill, depending on the direction you are heading. To measure steepness, as opposed to slope, you might sensibly take the absolute value of the slope or the square of the slope. Plot out the absolute value $|\partial H/\partial x|$ as a function of x and y. (Hint: the abs() function.) Plot out also the square: $(\partial H/\partial x)^2$

5. The above plots reflect the steepness only in the x direction. To get overall steepness, add up the steepness in the x and in the y directions. You can do this as either $|\partial H/\partial x| + |\partial H/\partial y|$ or as $\sqrt{(\partial H/\partial x)^2 + (\partial H/\partial y)^2}$.

6. Looking at your plot of overall steepness, find the steepest point in the original terrain, that is, the x and y at which the terrain is steepest.

For discussion:

- Why the square-root in the expression for steepness? (Hint: Think about the units.)

- Which do you think is more appropriate for measuring steepness: the sum of absolute values of slopes or the square-root of the sum of square slopes?

- Is it hard to find the x and y at which the function are steepest? How does the smoothness of the terrain compare to the smoothness of the steepness function?

Question for a computer programming class: Given a terrain function and initial location x_0 and y_0 as inputs, find the path followed by a drop of water as it rolls down the landscape.

Activity 2: How far does the car get?

Suppose you want to calculate the capacity of a road intersection regulated by a traffic light. One part of this calculation involves the distance that a car can travel, starting from a standstill, in a given amount of time.

Much of the information you have about the car is in the form of velocity. It's common sense that the velocity is 0 mph at the start and you can reasonably presume that the car accelerates to the speed limit of the road, say 30 mph. By doing a little observation, you can get an estimate for how many seconds it takes a typical car to reach the speed limit. For the present, let's say that it's 6 seconds.

- Construct a function (of time t) that models the velocity of the car and is consistent with the information specified above. Implement this as a computer function and graph it to verify that the velocity profile meets the specification. Here are several possible forms (with parameters that might be inappropriate).

```
v1 = makeFun(pmin(30, 30*t/6) ~ t)
v2 = makeFun(30*pnorm(t,mean=3,sd=1)~t)
v3 = makeFun(ifelse(t>6,30,30*t/6) ~ t)
```

- Compute the integral of the velocity function to get position. Plot out the position as a function of time. (Question: What should the from argument be? The to argument?)

- Does the result — how far the car goes — depend strongly on the details of the velocity function? Is there a strong reason to prefer one form of the function to the others? Make a quantitative argument either way.

Activity 3: Allocating resources for health care

The data file "jmm2012data1.csv" contains experts' evaluation of the number of Quality-Adjusted Life Years (QALYs) that will result from investment in two different health care options, A and B.

You can read in the file like this:

```
dat = fetchData("jmm2012data1.csv")
```

The data are discrete. You can construct a continuous, smooth function of QALYs versus expenditure for each of A and B like this:

```
fA = spliner(A~expend,data=dat,monotonic=TRUE)
fB = spliner(B~expend,data=dat,monotonic=TRUE)
```

You can now use fA and fB like any other function, for example, plotting

```
plotFun(fA(xA)~xA, xA.lim=range(0,50))
```

The problem. You have a total budget of 50 units to spend between A and B.

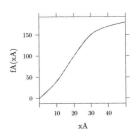

(a) What's the best allocation of the funding between A and B to maximize the QALY output?

(b) If your budget were increased slightly, what would be the resulting change in optimal QALY output? Put this in the form of a fraction: budget units per increased QALY.

(c) Suppose that you were mandated to spend at least 40 units of the budget on A. How would that additional constraint change the resulting optimal QALY output?

Activity 4

Here is an AP Calculus exam problem published by the College Board.

If the function f is defined by $f(x) = \sqrt{x^3 + 2}$, and g is an antiderivative of f such that $g(3) = 5$, then $g(1) =$?

(A) -3.268

(B) -1.585

(C) 1.732

(D) 6.585

(E) 11.585

You can use the antiD() operator to compute the antiderivative.

```
g = antiD(sqrt(x^2+2) ~ x)
```

The antiderivative is usually treated as an expression that involves some unknown additive constant C. One way to answer the question is to find the value of C consistent with $g(3) = 5$, then apply this in calculating $g(1)$.

Instructor Notes

This document is for instructors: people who are already very familiar with the mathematical concepts of calculus but who are new to R or perhaps generally to the use of computer software in teaching calculus.

Realize at the outset that computer notation you will be using is somewhat different from traditional mathematical notation:

- Operators are often written differently. Examples: x^2 or sqrt(x) or A*sin(2*pi*t/5). Students will make many mistakes at first, for example writing 2 t instead of 2*t, or leaving out parentheses to contain arguments (e.g., writing sin x rather than sin(x)).

- You give names to results so that you can use them in new places.

- Variable names are often multi-letter, latin, and use words rather than diacritical marks. Example: instead of $\hat{x}$ or p_0, write perhaps xestim or popInitial.

- An explicit functional style is used where the operator name is followed by a pair of parentheses. Within the parentheses, the various arguments are separated by commas, and often identified byname with a notation like x=3.

This last point marks an important difference between the computer notation and traditional notation, since in traditional position rather than a label is used to identify different inputs. For instance, in traditional notation you can write $\int_a^b f(x)dx$. In this notation, the operator is integration, a and b are arguments that mark the lower and upper bounds of integration, and depending on your philosophy, either $f(x)$ is the quantity being integrated (with dx denoting that x is the variable of integration), or $f(x)dx$ is the input to the integration operation. Similarly, in $\frac{df}{dx}$, the operation is differentiation, f is the function being differentiated, and the variable with respect to which the derivative is taken is identified by the dx as x.

In many calculus operations there is both a mathematical function and one or more variables with respect to which an operation is being performed. In English we often will say "with respect to," or "as a function of" or "versus". To mimic this in R, we have adopted a built-in R-language capability called a formula. The central component of a formula is the ~ symbol: "tilde."

To illustrate, here is the construction of a derivative:

```
D( sin(x^2) ~ x )

function (x)
cos(x^2) * (2 * x)
```

The computer has performed the derivative, producing a function of x.

Typically, you would perform this operation in order to use the resulting function for some purpose, so you should give the output a name:

```
fp = D( sin(x^2) ~ x )
```

To evaluate the function at a particular value of x, use the parentheses to pass along to fp the desired value for x:

```
fp( x=2 )

[1] -2.615
```

Or, perhaps you want to plot out the function for some range of x values:

```
plotFun( fp(x) ~ x, x.lim=range(0,4) )
```

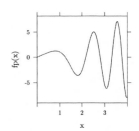

You might reasonably conclude that ~ turns an expression into a function. That's not quite right. The ~ provides a place to identify one or more symbolic

variables with respect to which the operation —
differentiation, plotting, etc. — is to take place. The ~
symbol is a way to organize symbolic information, not an
instruction to perform a particular calculus operation.

You must always specify explicitly the operation you
want to perform. If, for example, you want to create a
function, you can do so with the makeFun operator:

```
f = makeFun( sin(x^2) ~ x )
```

Notice that the operation has been named f, not $f(x)$
or some such thing. When you want to use the function,
you must give it an argument. If the argument is
numerical, just go ahead and put the numerical value in
parentheses:

```
f(x=3)
```

```
[1] 0.4121
```

If the argument is a symbol, and you're planning to
use that symbol as the variable in some calculus
operation, then you will want to use the ~ marker as well,
for example:

```
plotFun( f(x) ~ x, x.lim=range(0,4) )
```

or

```
F = antiD( f(x) ~ x )
```

Multiple Variables

In modeling-based calculus, it's appropriate to introduce
functions of multiple variables very early. The notation is
designed to make this straightforward. For example:

```
plotFun( exp(-t/10)*sin(2*pi*x/5) ~ x&t,
         x.lim=range(0,5), t.lim=range(0,10) )
```

When you create a function of multiple variables,
there's a question of how to identify which variable is
which. One traditional approach is to use a notation that

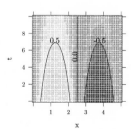

conveys both the name of the function and the arguments, e.g., $f(x, t) = e^{-t/10} \sin \frac{2\pi}{5} x$.

In the computer notation, the name is just f. The arguments are conveyed in the definition.

```
f = makeFun( exp(-t/10)*sin(2*pi*x/5) ~ x&t )
```

Perhaps it seems obvious from the definition that the first argument will be x and the second t. That happens to be true here, but it's not something to rely on. It's better to identify the arguments explicitly, e.g.

```
f( x=1, t=2 )
```

```
[1] 0.7787
```

```
f( t=2, x=1 )
```

```
[1] 0.7787
```

When you are using a function in a symbolic context, this can lead to a notation that looks, at first glance, to be redundant:

```
plotFun( f(t=t,x=2)~t, t.lim=range(0,10))
```

or, for example, to integrate with respect to x but leave things as a function of symbolic t:

```
F = antiD( f(t=t,x=x)~x )
```

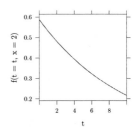

Symbolic Parameters

You can use symbols as parameters. The makeFun(), D(), antiD(), and plotFun() operators will recognize them and keep them in symbolic form. For instance:

```
D( A*exp(-k*t) ~ t )
```

```
function (t, A, k)
-(A * (exp(-k * t) * k))
```

However, when you want to evaluate such a function, including plotting it, you need to assign a numerical value to the parameter.

```
gp = D( A*exp(-k*t) ~ t )
plotFun( gp(t,A=2,k=1/10) ~ t, t.lim=range(0,20))
```

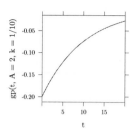

The Basic Calculus Operations

Differentiation and Partial Differentiation

```
D( a*x^2 + b*x + c ~ x )

function (x, a, b, c)
a * (2 * x) + b

D( a*x^2 + b*x + c ~ x&x )

function (x, a, b, c)
a * 2

D( a*x + b*y + c*x*y ~ x&y )

function (x, y, a, b, c)
c
```

Anti-Differentiation/Indefinite Integration

```
F = antiD(exp(x)*x^2 ~ x)
```

Evaluating an Anti-Derivative/Definite Integration

The anti-derivative function produced by antiD() has the same arguments as the input expression.

To compute an integral, evaluate the anti-derivative at the top and bottom of the interval of integration and subtract:

```
F(x=2) - F(x=1)

[1] 12.06
```

When integrating to $\pm\infty$, use the values -Inf or Inf.

The output of antiD() is arranged so that the "constant of integration" appears as an argument with a default value of zero. only the upper bound appears in the argument list. When a numerical approach is taken, the lower bound will be set to a default value. You can set the lower bound explicitly, if you wish, for instance:

```
F = antiD(exp(x)*x^2 ~ x)
F(x=2) # default const. of integration is  0

[1] 12.78

F(x=2, C=10) # setting const. of integration to 10

[1] 22.78
```

For some expressions, antiD() will compute the anti-derivative in symbolic form; the function returned will have familiar R notation. For all other input expressions, the output of antiD() is still a function, but it will not have an algebraic form. Instead, the function will compute an integral numerically.

The integral has an numerical interface that makes it operate as if it were an indefinite integral, but in fact the underlying calculation is always definite integration. In particularly, there is a default lower bound of zero. You need be concerned with the lower bound only if the default of zero is inappropriate. This can occur if there is a singularity in the expression being anti-differentiated at or near zero. You can specify a different lower bound by using the argument lower.bound when calling antiD().

You can use symbolic parameters in defining an anti-derivative, but they must be given numerical values at the time of evaluating it.

```
Fbell = antiD( dnorm(x,m=m,s=s) ~ x ) # symbolic s and m
Fbell(x=12,s=2,m=10) - Fbell(x=8,s=2,m=10)

[1] 0.6827
```

2.3 makeFun *versus* function

If you have used R extensively before, you may wonder
why makeFun() is being used rather than the more
conventional function(). In all the documentation for R,
after all, the standard way to define a function is
something like this:

```
f = function(x,y) { A + B*x^2 + C*y^2}
```

This is a very useful format for computer
programmers. It provides an explicit list of the
arguments, sets the order of the arguments, and allows
the function's body to refer to parameters that are defined
in an enclosing environment, e.g. the global environment.
The corresponding use of makeFun() goes like this:

```
g = makeFun(A + B*x^2 + C*y^2 ~ x&y)
```

The arguments are being identified as the variables
following the ~. But when makeFun() packages up a
function, it parses the body of the function for all variable
names and includes them as formal, named arguments to
the function:

The exception is the name pi,
which is treated as a constant
with value π.

```
g

function (x, y, A, B, C)
A + B * x^2 + C * y^2
```

This has some advantages for teaching mathematics
and statistics.

- Students can successfully use the system without
  having to learn or even be aware of the scoping rules
  of the language.

- The notation reinforces that variables and parameters
  are not intrinsically different.

- It avoids giving special status to an operator that
  happens to be called function and allows students to
  see as natural other operators that produce functions
  as output, e.g., fitModel(), D(), antiD(), rfun(), and
  so on.

Index